Published in 2006 in South Africa by
Rapid Phase (Pty) Ltd
24 3rd Avenue
Parktown North 2193
Johannesburg

 rapid phase

ISBN 0-620-37052-1

DTP by Dee Helling and Sandi Arrenbrecht
Printed by Creda Communications

OTHER MADAM & EVE BOOKS

MADAM & EVE APPEARS REGULARLY IN:
The Mail & Guardian, The Star, The Saturday Star, The Sunday Times, The EP Herald, The Mercury, The Natal Witness, The Daily Dispatch, The Cape Times, The Pretoria News, The Diamond Fields Advertiser, Die Volksblad, The Kokstad Advertiser, Vodaworld Magazine, The Namibian, The SA Times (London)

TO CONTACT MADAM & EVE:
POST: PO Box 413667, Craighall 2024, Johannesburg, South Africa
E-MAIL: madamandeve@rapidphase.co.za INTERNET: www.madamandeve.co.za

Madam & Eve

MADAMS of the CARIBBEAN

by Stephen Francis & Rico

rapid phase

By Stephen Francis & Rico

www.madamandeve.co.za

©RAPID PHASE - 2005

Extreme
CARTOON
MAKEOVER

Coming Soon to etv

6

MIELLLIES!!

CAN'T FIND YOUR **KATTY**, HUH? FOR FIVE BUCKS, SHERLOCK HOLMES WILL **SOLVE** THE CASE.

I ALWYS WONDERED WHY HE WORE THAT GOOFY HAT.

I DEDUCED THAT OUR WASHING MACHINE NEXT DOOR IS **BROKEN**. MIND IF I PUT THIS **T-SHIRT** IN YOUR WASH?

...NO SHIRT, SHERLOCK.

"NO **SHIRT**, **SHERLOCK**! HA-HA-HA! HEE-HEE! HOO-HOO!

MOM!!

I DON'T GET IT.

HEE-HEE.

MADAM & Eve

BY STEPHEN FRANCIS & RICO

HEY, THIS IS MY **LUCKY DAY!** A **TWENTY RAND NOTE** --RIGHT ON THE FLOOR.

www.madamandeve.co.za

POOF!

DON'T TAKE THAT MONEY, EVE. IT BELONGS TO MADAM!!

POOF!

DON'T BE A SUCKER, KID! FINDERS, KEEPERS. LOSERS, WEEPERS!

DON'T LISTEN TO HER! IT'S MADAM'S MONEY! IT BELONGS TO HER !!

POOF!

COMING UP-- "MAIDS WHO STEAL FROM THEIR MADAMS AND SEE IMAGINARY ANGELS AND DEVILS... ON THE NEXT JERRY SPRINGER!!

©RICO HAASE 2005

EVE!! DID YOU KNOW THERE'S A **HOLE** IN YOUR HANDBAG? YOUR MONEY'S FALLING OUT ALL OVER THE PLACE.

MORONS.

MIELLLIES!!

POOF!

MADAM, WOULD YOU **LEND** **MUGABE** **SIX BILLION** **RAND**?

ARE YOU CRAZY?! HE'S A BAD CREDIT RISK AND WILL SPEND IT UNWISELY!

I AGREE. WOULD YOU LEND ME **SIXTY** **RAND**?

NO WAY. YOU'RE A BAD CREDIT RISK AND WILL SPEND IT UNWISELY!

INTERNATIONAL FINANCE AND MADAMS NEVER MIX.

MUGABE & MBEKI: "SHOW AND TELL"

SHOW ME THE **MONEY!**

SHOW **ME** THE NEW CONSTITUTION!

SHOW ME THE MONEY!

SHOW **ME** THE ECONOMIC REFORMS!

SHOW ME THE MONEY!

SHOW ME THE **REPEAL** OF MEDIA-MUZZLING LAWS.

TELL ME I'M GETTING THE MONEY!

TELL **ME** YOU'RE NOT GIVING YOUR WIFE THE CREDIT CARD.

MUGABE & MBEKI: "SHOW AND TELL, PART 2"

SHOW ME THE **MONEY!!**

SHOW **ME** TRANSPARENCY.

SHOW ME THE MONEY!

SHOW **ME** LAWS PREVENTING LAND SEIZURES!

SHOW ME THE MONEY!

SHOW ME FREE AND FAIR **ELECTIONS** WITH **NO** INTIMIDATION OR VIOLENCE!

YOU'RE TAKING AWAY ALL MY CHECKS AND BALANCES! **HOW** DO YOU EXPECT ME TO RUN A **DEMOCRACY?!**

UH... LET'S TAKE A BREAK.

©RAPID PHASE · 2005

MUGABE AND MBEKI, THE NEGOTIATIONS CONTINUE...

SO... BASICALLY, YOU'RE SAYING THAT WHEN ZIMBABWEANS GO TO THE POLLS, I CAN'T **INTIMIDATE** THEM?

THAT'S RIGHT, BOB.

...HOW ABOUT "ONE VOTER, ONE PUNCH?"

NO, BOB.

NOT EVEN A FEW **HARSH WORDS** OR **THREATS** DIRECTED AT THEIR FAMILIES?

SORRY.

AND YOU CALL THIS "**FREE** AND **FAIR** ELECTIONS?"

YOU WANT THE LOAN OR NOT, BOB?

MBEKI AND MUGABE: THE NEGOTIATIONS CONTINUE...

OKAY, BOB. LET'S RECAP. ...NEW CONSTITUTION.

≧SIGH≧ AGREED.

FREEDOM OF SPEECH.

≧SIGH≧ AGREED.

FREE AND FAIR ELECTIONS.

BOB? FREE AND FAIR ELECTIONS?

BOY, YOU'RE REALLY MAKING ME JUMP THROUGH **HOOPS** FOR THIS LOUSY 500 MILLION.

HMMM.
OOO

I'D SAY THAT THIS PERSON IS STINGY... LIKES TO BUY SHOES... WATCHES TV ALL DAY...

... AND WON'T GIVE ANYONE A WAGE INCREASE EVEN IF THEY REALLY DESERVE IT.

THAT'LL BE TEN BUCKS.

HAND-WRITING ANALYSIS
Only 10 Rand

YOU SIT AROUND ALL DAY DOING NOTHING AND WATCH TV. YOU ALSO DRINK LOTS OF GIN & TONICS AND CHASE LOCAL HAWKERS.

THAT'LL BE TEN BUCKS.

SLAM!!

SHE WOULDN'T GO FOR IT.

HAND-WRITING ANALYSIS
Only 10 Rand

HMMM...

HAND-WRITING ANALYSIS
Only 10 Rand

JUDGING FROM THIS **SIGNATURE** ... THIS IS OBVIOUSLY A PERSON WHO IS DISCOURTEOUS TO OTHERS... DOESN'T BELIEVE IN ROAD SAFETY--

... AND TALKS ON THE CELLPHONE WHILE DRIVING.

HAND-WRITING ANALYSIS

HEY!! GIVE ME BACK MY **TRAFFIC TICKET!!**

YOU OWE HER TEN BUCKS.

MADAM & Eve

Domestic Proverbs

BY STEPHEN FRANCIS & RICO

A fool and his money are soon parted. (...then why is it so hard for me to get a **wage increase**?)

People who live in glass houses ...I'll never work for them.

The grass is always greener on the other side of the electrified fence.

A rolling stone gathers no moss. Anyway, who cares? That's the gardener's problem.

Let sleeping dogs lie.

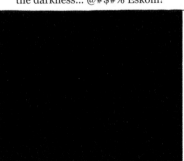

History repeats itself.

There's always a black sheep in the family.

© RAPID RUGGLE 2005

Better late than never.
Haste makes waste.
A watched pot never boils.

It's better to light a candle than curse the darkness... @#$#% Eskom!

MADAM & Eve

BY STEPHEN FRANCIS & RICO

The Top Secret Diary of Jacob Zuma

Dear Diary,
Was rudely awakened this A.M.
Without breakfast in bed!
And not by my maid either!

Oh. It's the SCORPIONS. They read me the search warrant as I put on my robe.

I decided to play it cool. After all, "they have a job to do." I offered them some coffee.

I changed my mind. What am I -- CRAZY? I called in my bodyguards!

A heated argument over "turf" errupted. A "stand off" over who should leave.

Military vehicles and lawyers arrived! WOW! This is better than television!

The Scorpions began seizing things. They seized my documents... they seized my bank records... and my Spiderman comic book collection...

Huh? They just seized my PEN! And now they're seizing my -- HEY! YOU CAN'T TAKE AWAY MY ____ ...

EVIDENCE
Top Secret Diary of Jacob Zuma

EXHIBIT B

Madam & Eve's

REALLY SCARY CONFLICTS

FREDDY vs JASON

ALIEN vs PREDATOR

SCORPIONS vs ZUMA

www.madamandeve.co.za

©RAPID PHASE - 2005

MADAM! "THE SCORPIONS" ARE HERE TO SEE YOU!

WHAT?!

ON SECOND THOUGHTS... PERHAPS THIS **ISN'T** SUCH A GOOD IDEA.

THE MOON IS IN PISCES... WHICH INDICATES AN UNFAVOURABLE TIME FOR CONFRONTATION. SEE YOU NEXT WEEK.

NEVER MIND. IT WAS JUST "THE **SCORPIOS.**"

www.madamandeve.co.za

©RAPID PHASE - 2005

...AND HERE COME THE **BODYGUARDS!** THEY LOOK ANGRY!

OH NO! THEY'VE GOT THE **SCORPIONS** IN A CHOKE HOLD!!

UNBELIEVABLE!! THEY'VE PULLED THE **REFEREE** INTO THE FRAY TOO!!

www.madamandeve.co.za

AND WE'LL BE BACK WITH MORE OF OUR SPECIAL TAG TEAM WRESTLING MATCH: **THE SCORPIONS** vs **THE ZUMA BODYGUARDS** ... AFTER THIS.

GREAT IDEA.

©RAPID PHASE - 2005

MADAM & Eve

BY STEPHEN FRANCIS & RICO

SPRING HAS SPRUNG! WE APOLOGISE FOR ANY INCONVENIENCE WHILE WE CONTINUE TO **RENEW** AND **REINVENT** OUR CARTOON STRIP.

RECYCLE

THIS CARTOON NOW DRAWN AND PRINTED ON RECYCLED PAPER

REFRESH

PSSSSSST!!

PSSSSSSH!!

RE-WRITE

RE-DRAW

REDESIGN

REWARD

www.madamandeve.co.za

RE-USE

©RAPID PHASE 2005

RE-RUN

REMIX

RELAX

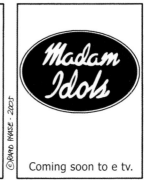

Coming soon to e tv.

MADAM & EVE

BY STEPHEN FRANCIS & RICO

AND NOW... WOULD YOU PLEASE WELCOME... TODAY'S **CELEBRITY CHEF** -- THAT GRANDMASTER OF GOURMETS -- FUNDI OF FOOD -- THE KING OF KINGKLIP --

-- ROBERT MUGABE!!

HI BOB. WELCOME TO THE SHOW.

THANKS, JENNY. GREAT TO BE HERE.

WHAT ARE YOU GOING TO MAKE TODAY?

POTATOES! THE STAPLE OF ANY HEALTHY DIET!!

YOU KNOW, IN MY COUNTRY... PEOPLE MAY BE **STARVING**, BUT ACTUALLY, WE HAVE **LOTS** OF THINGS TO EAT. POTATOES! HEAPS OF POTATOES!

TELL ME BOB: CAN ORDINARY ZIMBABWEANS EVEN **AFFORD** POTATOES?

FUNNY YOU SHOULD ASK THAT... IT JUST SO HAPPENS, I BROUGHT AN ORDINARY ZIMBABWEAN ALONG WITH ME TODAY.

...THAT BAG OF POTATOES YOU'RE HOLDING. DID YOU BUY IT YOURSELF?

UH...YES.

HA! TAKE **THAT** YOU TREACHEROUS WHITE COLONIAL BRITISH CONSPIRATORS!!

RIGHT. WHAT'S ON THE MENU, THEN?

WELL, I THOUGHT WE'D START WITH POTATO SOUP, AND POTATO PANCAKES... FOLLOWED BY POTATO GRATIN ALÁ MUGABE, POTATO SALAD, ... AND FINALLY POTATO PUDDING.

... AND WE'LL BE RIGHT BACK -- WITH MORE OF **"THE NAKED DESPOT"** ...AFTER THIS.

WHAT'S FOR DINNER? I FEEL LIKE POTATOES.

25

NEW PARLIAMENTARY FADS

FLOOR CROSSING

CROSS FLOOR CROSSING

CROSS-COUNTRY FLOOR CROSSING

FLOOR CROSS-DRESSING

AND, IN OTHER NEWS...

MORE FLOOR-CROSSING IN PARLIAMENT TODAY...

FLOOR CROSSING! **FLOOR CROSSING!** THAT'S _ALL_ YOU HEAR ABOUT THESE DAYS!!

IT'S NOT THE FLOOR **CROSSING** ...IT'S THE **FLOOR WASHING** I'M WORRIED ABOUT.

NAH.

DOMESTIC FLOOR-CROSSING JUST DOESN'T WORK.

AND IN OTHER NEWS, SOUTH AFRICA IS MOUNTING A MULTI-MILLION RAND DEFENCE AGAINST A **KILLER BIRD FLU** THAT COULD BE BROUGHT HERE BY MIGRATING WILD AQUATIC BIRDS FROM THE EAST.

BIRD FLU!! THE KILLER BIRD FLU IS COMING!!

WHEW

ACHOOO!!

SNIFF
EXCUSE ME.

AAAAAH!!

I HATE FRIDAYS.

MOM AND I WILL BE AWAY FOR THREE DAYS, EVE... SO YOU'RE ALL ON YOUR *OWN*.

HERE, I'VE MADE YOU AN ALPHABETISED **LIST** OF THINGS TO DO WHILE WE'RE GONE.

WHICH ACTIVITY ARE YOU GOING TO TACKLE FIRST?

THE **THREE DAY TEA BREAK.**

WHY IS SHE SMILING?

AH... THIS IS THE LIFE.

MADAM IS **AWAY** FOR **THREE DAYS**. I CAN DO WHATEVER I LIKE, AND THERE'S NO ONE TO ARGUE WITH OR TELL ME WHAT TO DO.

I'M SO BORED.

THIS IS SO GREAT. I'M **HOME ALONE**... NO MADAM OR MOTHER ANDERSON TO BOTHER ME FOR **THREE WHOLE DAYS!**

AAAAH!!

TAP! TAP! TAP!

I'M GOING TO GET HER FOR THIS.

WELL, WELL.
IF IT ISN'T THE
MAID WHO'S
HOME ALL
ALONE.

WONDERFUL.
TALKING
HOUSEHOLD
APPLIANCES.

LET'S
SEE
WHAT'S
IN THE
FRIDGE.

COME
ON!
I'LL
RACE
YOU
TO THE
KITCHEN!

THANK GOODNESS
MADAM COMES
BACK TOMORROW.

EVE!
WE'RE
HOME!!

GASP
IT CAN'T
BE!!

BUT IT **IS!**
IT'S REALLY **YOU!**
YOU'RE **BACK!**

GROUP HUG!

TOLD
YOU WE
WERE
AWAY
TOO
LONG!

MADAM & EVE

BY STEPHEN FRANCIS & RICO

AND IN OTHER NEWS...IT HAS BEEN REPORTED THAT PRESIDENT THABO MBEKI, A STAUNCH **CRITIC** OF **BOOM GATES**, WILL SOON BE LIVING IN **A GATED COMMUNITY** HIMSELF, TOGETHER WITH OTHER CABINET MINISTERS...

CODE BLUE. WE HAVE VISUAL ON THE BOOM GATE! STOP THE MOTORCADE!

SCREECH!

VUSI. CARL.

RIGHT. WE'LL CHECK **YOU** OUT...

THEN I'LL CHECK **YOU** OUT...

PAT PAT PAT

YOUR TURN.

NEED A PEN, SIR?

Name: _Thabo Mbeki_

Occupation: _President of South Africa_

Reason for visit: _Because I live here!_

© RAPID PHASE - 2005

RIGHT. EVERYTHING SEEMS TO BE IN ORDER...

IT'S A LONG WAIT TO FREEDOM, MISTER PRESIDENT.

OH, SHUT UP.

SNOOPING AROUND THE MAID'S ROOM

LOOK! ON TOP OF THE DRESSER. IT'S EVE'S **COFFEE CUP!**

OVER HERE ON THE TABLE! IT'S EVE'S **CELLPHONE.**

AND LOOK! UNDER THE DUVET ON THE BED! IT'S... ER, **EVE.**

©RAPID PHASE · 2005

I THOUGHT YOU SAID SHE WENT OUT.

WHAT ARE YOU TWO DOING IN MY ROOM?

www.madamandeve.co.za

RIGHT. YOU WANT TO TELL ME WHAT THE TWO OF YOU WERE DOING **SNOOPING** AROUND MY ROOM?!

©RAPID PHASE · 2005

www.madamandeve.co.za

WE'RE... IN **EVE'S** ROOM?! THIS IS... **YOUR** ROOM?!

AND DON'T HAND ME THE OLD "SLEEP-WALKING ROUTINE," EITHER!!

SNORE

SNORE

Panel 1: LEARN "SPIN" The 12th Official Language

Panel 2: WHAT'S "SPIN"?

IT'S A WAY TO INTEGRATE RELATIONAL COMMUNICATION ONTOLOGIES WHILE EMPOWERING USER-CENTRIC ABSTRACTIONS.

Panel 3: WHAT THE HELL DID SHE JUST SAY?

Panel 4: IT'S SUCH A BEAUTIFUL LANGUAGE.

Panel 5: READY FOR YOUR FIRST LESSON IN "SPIN"? REPEAT AFTER ME.

LEARN "SPIN" The 12th Official Language Only 10 Rand

Panel 6: IT'S TIME TO EXPEDITE TRANSPARENT EMPOWERMENT PARADIGMS TO ENABLE TRANSFORMATIONAL COMPETITIVE FISCAL MODELS.

IT'S TIME TO EXPEDITE TRANSPARENT EMPOWERMENT PARADIGMS TO ENABLE TRANSFORMATIONAL COMPETITIVE FISCAL MODELS.

Panel 7: WHAT DID I JUST SAY?

YOU JUST GIVE ME A BIG RAISE.

Panel 8: **WHAT?!**

RELAX. JUST A LITTLE "SPIN" HUMOUR.

Panel 9: CONGRATULATIONS. YOU ARE NOW FLUENT IN THE LANGUAGE OF "SPIN." HERE'S YOUR DIPLOMA.

Panel 10: CLICK

Panel 11: AND IN OTHER NEWS, A GOVERNMENT SPOKESMAN SAID THAT THE COUNTRY NEEDS TO INCENTIVISE PROBABILISTIC CROSS-PLATFORM MARKETS, WHILE INTEGRATING WORLD-CLASS BACK-END SYNERGIES.

Panel 12: IT'S EASIER TO SPEAK THAN TO UNDERSTAND.

MADAM & Eve

BY STEPHEN FRANCIS & RICO

Men in Black
The Zuma Trial Spring Fashion Preview

Zuming along in classic black.

Accessorise... and arrive in style!*

* Transportation by Humvee

"No photos, please!!" *

* Sunglasses by Prado. Communication earpieces by HiFi Warehouse

At work... at play... and in front of the court... stand out from the crowd with fashionable casualwear.

ZUMA 100% INNOCENT

I ♥ ZUMA

The Magistrate

...dress for judicial success!

Senior council... always stylish for the defense!*

* Handcrafted leather briefcases by Guccy.

The final verdict: So elegant, it ought to be illegal!

CORRUPTION

by Calvin Kleen

Fashions and accessories to silence any courtroom.

NEXT MONTH:
This Summer, break out in bright ORANGE!

39

HELLO?

YES. I WAS WONDERING, WHAT IS THE RECORD FOR "LONGEST LIE ON AN IRONING BOARD?"

THIRTY HOURS?! THAT'S ALL?!

SHE'S GOING FOR THE GUINNESS BOOK OF RECORDS.

PIECE OF CAKE.

EVE'S TRYING FOR THE GUINNESS BOOK OF RECORDS: LONGEST LIE-DOWN ON AN IRONING BOARD.

HOW LONG BEFORE SHE BREAKS THE RECORD?

GET REAL! FIRST SHE HAS TO TRAIN AND GET IN SHAPE!

TWEET! TIME!

HOW AM I DOING?

STILL TOO TENSE.

STILL PRACTISING FOR THE GUINNESS BOOK OF RECORDS?

ANOTHER FEW DAYS OF TRAINING AND SHE'S ALMOST READY.

WE'VE THOUGHT OF EVERYTHING. WE'VE LEFT NOTHING TO CHANCE.

...SUPPOSE IN THE MIDDLE OF "GOING FOR THE WORLD RECORD..." EVE HAS TO GO TO THE BATHROOM?

SEE THIS LONG PLASTIC TUBE?

I'M OUTTA HERE.

:TWEET: AND... TIME!!

:WHEW: HOW AM I DOING?

LOOKING GOOD.

KEEP ON TRAINING THIS HARD AND THE GUINNESS WORLD RECORD FOR LONGEST LIE-DOWN ON AN IRONING BOARD IS IN THE BAG. OKAY-- HIT THE SHOWERS!

©RAPID PHASE - 2005

www.madamandeve.co.za

THIS IS IT -- EVE'S GOING FOR THE GUINNESS BOOK OF RECORDS: LONGEST LIE-DOWN ON AN IRONING BOARD. SIXTEEN HOURS AND COUNTING.

©RAPID PHASE - 2005

YOU GIVE HER FOOD OR WATER AND I'LL KILL YOU.

www.madamandeve.co.za

It's for the neighbour's Halloween party. Do you think everyone will believe us as "TWO SCARY WITCHES"?

...WELL?

SO MANY RESPONSES, SO LITTLE TIME.

BOO!!

..."SCARED" YOU, DIDN'T I?

IS THAT MY PILLOWCASE?

YES... SO?

SLAM!!

SOME PEOPLE DON'T SEEM TO BE GETTING INTO THE HALLOWEEN SPIRIT.

TRICK OR TREAT! HAPPY HALLOWEEN!!

NOT SO FAST. WHERE ARE YOUR COSTUMES?!

WE'RE DRESSED UP AS "PREVIOUSLY DISADVANTAGED AND DISPLACED AFRICAN YOUTHS, NOW LIVING IN A WHITE ENCLOSED NEIGHBOURHOOD."

SLAM!!

...TOLD YOU I SHOULD HAVE GONE AS SPIDERMAN.

44

MADAM & EVE

BY STEPHEN FRANCIS & RICO

WHAT ARE YOU DOING HERE?

DUH.

WHAT AM I "DOING" HERE? I DON'T KNOW... WHAT ARE WE ALL DOING HERE?

I BELIEVE IT WAS HENRY DAVID THOREAU WHO SAID WE ARE HERE TO: "SIMPLIFY, SIMPLIFY."

OR AS EXISTENTIALIST FRIEDRICH NIETZCHE SAYS, WE ARE HERE TO EXPERIENCE "LIFE THROUGH THE WORLD WE LIVE IN."

... WE MUST CONSTANTLY STRIVE FOR A SERIES OF "NOBLE AND DELICATE EXPERIENCES."

AND FINALLY, IT IS OUR DUTY TO LIVE LIFE IN ITS ENTIRETY... AND TO PURSUE A SERIES OF DEFINED MORALITIES, IF WE ARE TO SHAPE OUR DESTINY.

© RAPID PHASE - 2005

... SO MAYBE THE REAL QUESTION ISN'T: "WHAT AM I DOING HERE?" ... BUT RATHER: "WHAT ARE YOU TWO DOING HERE?!"

MAYBE SOMEONE SHOULD TELL HER IT'S HER DAY OFF TODAY.

NAH.

Panel 1: YOU **DID**, DIDN'T YOU? — NO, I DIDN'T.

Panel 2: YES YOU **DID**. — NO, I **DIDN'T**!

Panel 3: OH, COME **ON**! YOU **DID**! — ...DID **NOT**!!

Panel 4: IT'S SO HARD THESE DAYS TO FIND SOMEONE WHO **VOTED** FOR THE **NATS**. — DON'T LOOK AT ME.

Panel 5: I DON'T KNOW.

Panel 6: COME ON. **GO** FOR IT. — I DON'T KNOW. WHAT IF I **LIKE** IT?

Panel 7: JUST TRY IT OUT. SEE WHAT YOU THINK... — WELL... IF YOU'RE **SURE**...

Panel 8: WOW. — GIVE IT A FEW MINUTES. IT GETS EVEN **MORE** COMFORTABLE.

Panel 9: BEE WORLD — RIGHT. NOW LET'S TRY ON THE PROTECTIVE HEAD GEAR.

Panel 10: DO YOU HAVE ANY **THICKER** GLOVES?

Panel 11: YOU DON'T **NEED** THEM. THE BEES CAN'T STING THROUGH THOSE. — WHO SAID ANYTHING ABOUT BEES?

Panel 12: OUR MAID'S ON LEAVE AND WE HAVE TO CLEAN THE **OVEN**. — YOU SELL BLOW-TORCHES HERE?

MADAM & EVE

BY STEPHEN FRANCIS & RICO

AND, IN OTHER NEWS... SURVEYS REPORT THAT CORRUPTION IS AT AN ALL TIME HIGH...

...MAKING THIS A **BLACK** DAY IN S.A. HISTORY.

YOU SEE **THAT**? IT'S A **RACIST** METAPHOR!

WHAT DO YOU MEAN?

NO WONDER WE'RE "PREVIOUSLY DISADVANTAGED"! ANYTHING "**BLACK**" AUTOMATICALLY MEANS **BAD**!

... BLACK **HEART**! BLACK **MAGIC**! BLACK **SHEEP**! BLACK **WIDOW**! BLACK **SPOT**!

I DUNNO. I GOT "**BLACKJACK**" ONCE AND WON LOTS OF MONEY.

...WHILE ANYTHING "WHITE" AUTOMATICALLY MEANS "WONDERFUL" AND "PURE."

...WHITE **WEDDING**! WHITE **LIGHT**! WHITE **DIAMOND**! WHITE **CHRISTMAS**!

AND, IN OTHER DISAPPOINTING NEWS...

WATCH. HERE WE GO **AGAIN**! "...THINGS LOOK **BLACK**."

...CONCERNS WERE RAISED IN PARLIAMENT TODAY THAT THE PLANNED 20 BILLION RAND **GAUTRAIN** LINKING PRETORIA AND JOHANNESBURG COULD END UP BECOMING A HUGE, EXPENSIVE **WHITE** ELEPHANT.

AH-HA!!

© RAPID PHASE - 2005

The SEVEN HABITS of highly effective GOGOS

PAMPHLET GUYS AT ROBOTS CAN BE ANNOYING.

WHEN THEY HAND YOU A PAMPHLET, TAKE IT.

THEN AT THE NEXT ROBOT, HAND YOUR **FIRST** PAMPHLET TO THE **SECOND** PAMPHLET GUY...

AND THEN, AT THE NEXT ROBOT, HAND THE **SECOND** PAMPHLET TO THE **THIRD** PAMPHLET GUY... AND SO FORTH...

TRY IT, IT'S **FUN**!! ... AND THE NEXT TIME THEY SEE YOU, THEY'LL THINK TWICE ABOUT GIVING YOU A PAMPHLET.

The SEVEN HABITS of highly effective GOGOS

ALL US REAL SOUTH AFRICANS LOVE OUR **BOEREWORS**

BUT WHO WANTS TO BE LAST IN THE BRAAI QUEUE?

THAT'S WHEN YOU GET YOURSELF AN EXTRA LONG STICK, PLACE THE SAUSAGE ON ONE END, AND...

ZAP!

...LET YOUR ELECTRIFIED FENCE DO ALL THE WORK.

The SEVEN HABITS of highly effective GOGOS

BEING A GOGO IN SOUTH AFRICA TODAY ISN'T EASY. SOMETIMES PEOPLE MAKE INAPPROPRIATE **JOKES**... ESPECIALLY WHEN I'M ON MY CELLPHONE.

HEY!! **YEBO GOGO!** HAHAHAHAHA!!

POW!

REMEMBER... GOGOS ARE PEOPLE TOO. DON'T BE A **GOGOIST!**

OW.

The SEVEN HABITS of highly effective GOGOS

 SCHIZOPHRENIC HOMELESS PEOPLE THAT TALK TO THEM-SELVES CAN BE <u>SCARY</u>.

THE ALIEN INVASION IS NEAR! THE MONKEYS THREW A COCONUT AT MY HEAD!!

 I LIKE TO GIVE THEM A BLUETOOTH EARPIECE.

 THAT WAY, NOBODY EVEN **NOTICES**.

THE ALIEN INVASION IS NEAR! THE MONKEYS THREW A COCONUT AT MY HEAD!

© RAPID PHASE - 2005

The SEVEN HABITS of highly effective GOGOS

 IF YOU'RE A REAL GOGO LIKE <u>ME</u>... YOU LOVE TO <u>KNIT</u>!

 VOILÁ!

 BIG DEAL. WHAT GOOD IS IT TO **KNIT** JUST **ONE** SOCK?

WHO SAID IT'S A "SOCK"?

© RAPID PHASE - 2005

MADAM & Eve

BY STEPHEN FRANCIS & RICO

HEY, LOOK!

TAKE A LOOK AT THIS. IT'S THE **TWENTY YEAR ANNIVERSARY** OF THE **MAIL & GUARDIAN** THIS WEEK.

IMAGINE _THAT._

WE SHOULD DO SOMETHING **SPECIAL** TO **COMMEMORATE** THE OCCASION.

I AGREE. SOMETHING REALLY **AMAZING** AND **SURPRISING.**

www.madamandeve.co.za

WAIT A MINUTE... I'VE GOT IT! ...WHEN WAS THE **LAST TIME** WE GAVE **EVE** A **RAISE?**

LET'S SEE... ACCORDING TO MY RECORDS...

...EXACTLY **TWENTY YEARS** AGO!

EVE!!

YES, MADAM?

...SEND A NICE **FRUITCAKE** TO THE _MAIL & GUARDIAN._

MAKE IT A SMALL ONE.

HAPPY **20TH** ANNIVERSARY **M&G**

52

MADAM & EVE

BY STEPHEN FRANCIS & RICO

IT'S NOW TIME FOR TODAY'S FEATURE RACE AT KENILWORTH -- THE **PARLIAMENTARY HANDICAP**!

HUH?

THEY'RE AT THE GATE... AND THEY'RE OFF!!

JUMPING OUT IN THE LEAD IS **VOTER'S PROMISE** WITH **LOFTY IDEALS** CLOSE BEHIND! IT'S **VOTER'S PROMISE** AND **LOFTY IDEALS**...

BUT WAIT!! HERE COMES **REALITY CHECK** -- WITH **LOFTY IDEALS** FALLING AWAY QUICKLY! AND HERE COMES **BEHIND CLOSED DOORS**!

INTO THE CLUBHOUSE TURN -- IT'S **BEHIND CLOSED DOORS**, FOLLOWED BY **POLITICAL FOOTBALL**, **SMEAR CAMPAIGN** AND **RACE CARD**!!

COME ON, RACE CARD!!

AND... IT'S **RACE CARD** OUT IN FRONT... FOLLOWED BY **CROSS THE FLOOR** AND **NEPOTISM**!! BUT WAIT!! HERE COMES **CORRUPTION**!!

IT'S **CORRUPTION** AND **ARMS DEAL** NECK AND NECK -- FOLLOWED INTO THE HOME STRETCH BY **I RESIGN** AND **YOU'RE UNDER ARREST**!!

AND... IT'S A **PHOTO FINISH**! AT THE WIRE -- IT'S **I RESIGN**, HERE COME THE SCORPIONS AND **YOU'RE UNDER ARREST**!!

WHEW.

©RAPID PHASE · 2005

AND NOW... LET'S GO TO OUR NEXT TELEVISED RACE -- THE **DOMESTIC HANDICAP**...

AND THEY'RE OFF! IT'S **CHRISTMAS BONUS**, FOLLOWED BY **MAID'S DAY OFF**... WITH **WAGE INCREASE** OUT IN FRONT!

COME ON, WAGE INCREASE!!

SIGH! I HATE CLEANING THE OVEN.

THAT'S ODD. IT SEEMS TO GO ON FOREVER BACK HERE! HEY-- WHAT'S THAT?-- A DOOR! I NEVER SAW THAT BEFORE.

CREAK

HUH?

INCREDIBLE!! BEHIND THE OVEN --SOME KIND OF PARALLEL UNIVERSE! IT'S ... IT'S...

NEXT: YES, IT'S -- SISULU IN WONDERLAND!

SISULU IN WONDERLAND

THIS IS INCREDIBLE! A WHOLE WORLD EXISTS BEHIND MADAM'S OVEN.

IT'S LIKE SOUTH AFRICA... ONLY IN MANY WAYS... STRANGELY DIFFERENT.

LOTS OF WORK LOTS OF MONEY CAN I HELP YOU?

I MUST BE IN A PARALLEL UNIVERSE!

NAME.

...OKAY, AN ENCLOSED PARALLEL UNIVERSE.

SISULU IN WONDERLAND

GASP! IT'S THE WHITE RABBIT!

I'M LATE! FOR A VERY IMPORTANT DATE!

NO WE'RE NOT.

...THIS IS MY EMPOWERMENT PARTNER... THE BLACK RABBIT.

IT'S SOME KIND OF STRANGE PARALLEL UNIVERSE! I'VE GONE THROUGH THE LOOKING GLASS.

AH. THAT'S MORE LIKE IT. ... TEA BREAK!

DRINK ME

NEXT: THE EVIL QUEEN OF HEARTS

SISULU IN WONDERLAND

EVE--TRAPPED IN A STRANGE **PARALLEL** UNIVERSE!

ACTUALLY--IT'S NOT SO BAD HERE. I COULD GET **USED** TO IT.

ALL HAIL!! MAKE WAY FOR THE QUEEN OF HEARTS!!

UH-OH.

HALT!!

WHY IS THIS SUBJECT NOT BOWING AND SCRAPING?

TEA BREAK.

SISULU IN WONDERLAND

I NEED A NEW HANDMAIDEN. SHE'LL DO. THE **QUEEN OF HEARTS** HAS SPOKEN!

BUT YOUR ROYALNESS! I DON'T **BELONG** HERE! I'M A DOMESTIC WORKER FROM A **PARALLEL UNIVERSE** THAT ENTERED THIS WORLD THROUGH A DOOR IN THE BACK OF MADAM'S OVEN.

OH, SURE... LIKE I REALLY BELIEVE **THAT** ONE. **OFF WITH HER HEAD!!**

I WANT MY LAWYER!!

SISULU IN WONDERLAND

HAS EVE ENTERED SOME MYSTERIOUS PARALLEL UNIVERSE?

SCREEECH!!

EXCUSE ME. I DIDN'T SEE YOU, BECAUSE PERHAPS I WAS DRIVING TOO **FAST**. I APOLOGISE.

COME TO THINK OF IT, MAYBE IT'S TIME I REPLACED MY **TYRES**, MADE MY VEHICLE **ROADWORTHY**... AND DROVE MORE **CAREFULLY**.

EVERYONE GET OUT. I'M **REFUNDING** YOUR MONEY.

YEP, IT'S A PARALLEL UNIVERSE, ALL RIGHT!

SISULU IN WONDERLAND

EVE IS TRAPPED IN A STRANGE **PARALLEL UNIVERSE**...

HEY **YOU**! GASP

IS THIS **YOURS**? SOMEONE DROPPED A **WALLET** WITH A WAD OF MONEY IN IT.

UH... NO, IT'S **NOT** MINE.

EXCUSE ME, DID YOU DROP THIS?

I WANNA GO **HOME**!!

SISULU IN WONDERLAND

GASP MADAM!!

ARE YOU MY **REAL** MADAM... OR A MADAM FROM A **PARALLEL UNIVERSE**?

I DON'T KNOW WHAT YOU'RE TALKING ABOUT-- BUT HERE'S YOUR WAGE INCREASE FOR THIS WEEK.

NOW. **WHAT** WERE YOU SAYING?

NEVER MIND. I THINK I'LL STAY HERE A WHILE.

TAKE THE DAY OFF IF YOU WANT.

WHILE YOU'RE AT IT, TAKE THE DAY OFF.

TAKE THE DAY OFF? GIVING ME A RAISE EVERY WEEK? I **MUST** BE STUCK IN A STRANGE PARALLEL UNIVERSE!

...THINGS ARE THE SAME, YET SOMEHOW COMPLETELY **DIFFERENT.**

EVE, IF YOU WOULDN'T MIND;- PLEASE BRING MY MOTHER A **RUM & COKE.**

GASP! I'VE **FOUND** IT! THE DOOR **OUT** OF THIS WEIRD **PARALLEL** UNIVERSE!

WHEW FINALLY. **HOME.**

OH, GOOD, MADAM. YOU'RE BACK.

WOULD YOU LIKE A CUP OF TEA? I'M JUST BUSY WITH THE LAUNDRY.

OH GREAT, ... A PARALLEL, **PARALLEL,** UNIVERSE.

MADAM & Eve

BY STEPHEN FRANCIS & RICO

"TODAY, I WAS CHARGED BY THE NATIONAL PROSECUTING AUTHORITY, FOLLOWING ALLEGATIONS OF RAPE THAT WERE MADE AGAINST ME LAST MONTH."

"MY APPEARANCE IN COURT COMES AFTER FOUR WEEKS OF INTENSE AND DISTORTED MEDIA REPORTS ON THIS ISSUE."

CREAK!

UNCLE JACOB. IS THAT YOU?

YES. I WAS JUST CHECKING TO MAKE SURE YOU HAD ENOUGH DUVETS.

"I WISH TO STATE CLEARLY THAT I AM INNOCENT OF THESE CHARGES."

OOPS! I TRIPPED ON THE RUG!

TRIP!

OW! WHERE'D THAT **TABLE** COME FROM?!

CRASH!

"I ABHOR ANY KIND OF ABUSE AGAINST WOMEN."

WHOOPSIE.

FWUMP!

EXCUSE ME. THIS IS A VERY EMBARRASSING ACCIDENT.

"I APPRECIATE THAT THIS MATTER IS NOW BEFORE THE COURT AND I AM CONFIDENT THAT IT WILL BE BROUGHT TO ITS FINALITY."

OW, MY BACK! I CAN'T MOVE!

UNCLE?

LOOK OUT! IT'S AN EARTHQUAKE!!

©RICO RAASE-2005

AND THAT'S HOW IT **REALLY** HAPPENED.

MAYBE WE CAN GET A LONG POSTPONEMENT.

EVERY YEAR IT'S THE SAME THING! EVERY YEAR THEY GET AWAY SCOTT FREE! AM I **RIGHT**?!!

SIR! YES, SIR!

© RICO PHASE - 2005

AS FOR **THIS** YEAR?!!

SIR! THIS YEAR IT'S GOING TO BE DIFFERENT, SIR!!

DAMN RIGHT!! NOW GO OUT THERE AND MAKE ME PROUD! -- AND DON'T COME BACK **EMPTYHANDED**!!

SIR! YES, SIR!!

www.madamandeve.co.za

IT'S BEGUN... "OPERATION 'GLEN ANDERSON DUSTBIN MEN CHRISTMAS BONUS' IS UNDERWAY.

THAT'S ODD. NOBODY TOOK THE DUSTBIN OUT TO THE STREET.

GOOD MORNING, MRS ANDERSON!! WE'RE YOUR **DUSTBIN MEN**! MERRY CHRISTMAS!!

BATTLE STATIONS!!

SLAM!!

:SQUAWK: EAGLE'S NEST TO BASE: THE SUBJECT HAS FLED. I REPEAT: THE SUBJECT HAS **FLED**.

www.madamandeve.co.za © RAPID PHASE - 2005

PHASE ONE IS NEGATIVE, SIR!

RIGHT. LET'S MOVE TO PHASE **TWO**.

HEAD FOR THE BACK! THE DUSTBIN MEN ARE AT THE FRONT OF THE HOUSE!!

:WHEW: ...THAT WAS A **CLOSE ONE**, HUH, EVE?

www.madamandeve.co.za © RAPID PHASE - 2005

DID YOU CALL ME ..."EVE"?

PLOP!

MERRY CHRISTMAS... FROM YOUR DUSTBIN MEN.

HELP!! THEY'VE BREACHED THE PERIMETER!!

CREAK

HAPPY HOLIDAYS, MRS ANDERSON! FROM ALL YOUR **DUSTBIN MEN!!**

GASP

--AND **HAPPY HOLIDAYS** TO **YOU!!** --HERE'S A VERY **GENEROUS** CHRISTMAS BONUS!

"THE ELEMENT OF TOTAL SURPRISE WILL VANQUISH ALL FOES." -- SUN SZU, THE ART OF WAR

www.madamandeve.co.za ©RAPID PHASE - 2005

MEN! THIS IS A **VICTORY** FOR DUSTBIN MEN EVERYWHERE! AFTER YEARS OF TRYING, WE FINALLY GOT A **CHRISTMAS BONUS** FROM GWEN AND EDITH ANDERSON!

HEAR! HEAR! CLAP! CLAP! CLAP! CLAP! CLAP! CLAP!

THIS IS A CAUSE FOR CELEBRATION! SO... RAISE YOUR GLASSES AND--

UH... SHOULDN'T WE OPEN UP THE ENVELOPE **FIRST,** SIR?

©RAPID PHASE - 2005

"CONGRATULATIONS... YOU HAVE WON **EITHER** A NEW CAR, CD PLAYER, OR A WEEKEND FOR TWO AT--"

HEY!! THEY GAVE US A **TIME SHARE LETTER!!**

REVENGE... IS A DISH BEST SERVED COLD. THEN TOSSED IN THE DUSTBIN.

FA LA LA LA LA LA LA LA LA.

www.madamandeve.co.za

HOLIDAYS... OR NO HOLIDAYS... YOU SHOULD KNOW BETTER THAN TO TALK ON YOUR **CELLPHONE** WHILE DRIVING. HERE'S YOUR **TICKET!**

AND WHILE YOUR AT IT, WHERE'S MY **CHRISTMAS BONUS?**

...**CHRISTMAS BONUS?!**

HEY!! YOU THINK IT'S **EASY** HANDING OUT **TRAFFIC FINES** TO MOTORISTS ALL YEAR?! IT'S TIME FOR A LITTLE **APPRECIATION!!**

AND IN OTHER NEWS... A WOMAN WAS ARRESTED TODAY WHEN SHE **ATTACKED** A TRAFFIC COP, OVER WHAT AUTHORITIES ARE NOW CALLING..."**CHRISTMAS BONUS RAGE."**

HEY, THAT LOOKS LIKE...

EVE... HERE'S YOUR... ...**WAIT**...

--EVE!! HERE'S YOUR... HERE'S YOUR...

...HERE'S YOUR CH... YOUR CH... YOUR C-C-CHRI--

"**BONUS!!** -- HERE'S YOUR CHRISTMAS **BONUS!**" --IT'S NOT THAT HARD, GWEN! YOU'RE **BLOCKING.**

⸨CHOKE⸩ I **CAN'T** DO IT!!

EVE -- HERE IT IS: YOUR CHRISTMAS BONUS! HERE'S YOUR **CHRISTMAS BONUS!**

I **DID** IT! I **DID** IT!! DOCTOR-- I'M **CURED!!**

I'M PROUD OF YOU. HERE'S MY BILL.

UH... I THINK THERE'S SOME MISTAKE. YOU CHARGED ME FOR AN **EXTRA** SESSION.

NO MISTAKE. THAT'S FOR **MY** CHRISTMAS BONUS!

AND IN OTHER NEWS, A WOMAN WAS **ARRESTED** TODAY AFTER ATTEMPTING TO **STRANGLE** HER **PSYCHIATRIST**, IN WHAT EXPERTS ARE CALLING "CHRISTMAS BONUS RAGE."

HEY! THAT LOOKS EXACTLY LIKE ...

...FOR THE LAST MONTH, THE **ZUMA RAPE COMPLAINT** WAS SHROUDED IN SECRECY.

CLUNK!

JACOB ZUMA FINALLY APPEARED IN COURT THIS WEEK... A **MONTH** AFTER THE ALLEGED OFFENSE TOOK PLACE.

CLUNK!

IN ADDITION, ZUMA'S HEARING WAS HELD IN **SECRECY.** HIS PERSONAL BODYGUARDS **BARRED** MEMBERS OF THE PUBLIC AND JOURNALISTS FROM ATTENDING. THIS BEGS THE QUESTION: HAVE THE SCALES OF JUSTICE BEEN **TIPPED?!**

CLUNK!

WILL YOU PLEASE STOP DOING THAT?!!

CLUNK!

GO AHEAD -- JUST **TRY** AND BRING ME DOWN! I HAVE THE BEST **LAWYERS!** THE TOUGHEST **BODYGUARDS!!**

I HAVE THE **PEOPLE** ON MY SIDE!! I HAVE --

STOMP!

SPLORTCH!!

KING KONG
VS
JACOB ZUMA

Coming Soon to a Cinema near you.

AND... IN OTHER NEWS, **KING KONG** HAS ATTACKED SOUTH AFRICA!!

ACCORDING TO LATEST REPORTS, THE **GIANT APE** HAS GRABBED A GOLDEN-HAIRED WOMAN!

I HATE THE SILLY SEASON.

I **TOLD** YOU!! NO MORE CHRISTMAS BONUSES! GOT THAT?!

GRONK?

66

Panel 1: WE'RE COMING TO YOU LIVE FROM A MAJOR SHOPPING MALL ...WHERE A YOUNG GIRL HAS TURNED SANTA'S GROTTO INTO A BLACK ECONOMIC EMPOWERMENT PROTEST.

Panel 2: I'M TIRED OF "DREAMING OF A WHITE CHRISTMAS!!" WHERE 'RE ARE YOUR **BEE** CREDENTIALS?!... AND TALK ABOUT **WINDOW DRESSING!** -- ONLY **ONE** BLACK ELF!!

Panel 3: MORE BLACK ELVES!! MORE BLACK ELVES!!

Panel 4: MORE BLACK ELVES!! MORE BLACK ELVES!!

HEY!! I DIDN'T EVEN GET TO TELL HIM WHAT I WANT FOR CHRISTMAS YET!!

JUST KEEP WALKING.

www.madamandeve.co.za

© RAPID PHASE - 2005

Panel 5: I DON'T KNOW, DOCTOR. IT'S THIS TIME OF YEAR. EVERYONE STARTS ACTING A LITTLE CRAZY.

© RAPID PHASE - 2005

Panel 6: JUST BECAUSE IT'S THE CHRISTMAS HOLIDAYS, PEOPLE SEEM TO --

Panel 7: GO ON.

Panel 8: I HATE LYING ON THE COUCH DURING THE **SILLY SEASON.**

www.madamandeve.co.za

'TWAS THE NIGHT BEFORE CHRISTMAS AND ALL THROUGH THE HOUSE...

NOT A CREATURE WAS STIRRING NOT EVEN A MOUSE...

THE POST HAD PILED UP THE LIGHT TIMER CLICKED ON.

EVERYONE ON VACATION THE FAMILY LONG GONE.

THE BURGLARS ARRIVED AS THE HOUR GREW LATE.

AND VERY CAREFULLY CUT THE ELECTRIFIED GATE.

MOM!!
WHAT?! SO I SOUTH AFRICANISED IT A LITTLE!!

YOU BETTER WATCH OUT! YOU BETTER NOT CRY. YOU BETTER NOT POUT -- I'M TELLING YOU WHY, SANTA CLAUS IS COMING TO TOWN!!

"HE KNOWS WHEN YOU'RE SLEEPING."

"HE KNOWS WHEN YOU'RE AWAKE..."

"HE KNOWS IF YOU'VE BEEN BAD OR GOOD, SO BE GOOD FOR GOODNESS SAKE!"

FATHER CHRISTMAS IS A STALKER!!

MOM!!

THUD! THUD! THUD! BIFF! BOFF! THWACK! POW! THUD! THWUP!! THUD! THWUP!! THUD! THWUP!!

DING! DING!

OKAY! GOOD FIGHT. GO TO YOUR CORNERS!

SOMEHOW, I DON'T THINK THIS IS HOW BOXING DAY IS MEANT TO BE CELEBRATED.

THE FATHER CHRISTMAS CHRISTMAS BONUS SCAM

HO HO HO. SATISFIED WITH THE JOB I'VE BEEN DOING?

ARMED RESPONSE

IT'S INCREDIBLE!!

I ALWAYS THOUGHT YOU COULD IRON IN ONLY **ONE** DIRECTION -- BUT ACTUALLY YOU CAN IRON BACK AND FORTH, **BACK** AND **FORTH!!**

GAVE IT TO HER FOR CHRISTMAS.

DOMESTIC WORK FOR DUMMIES

WHAT'S THE SIMILARITY BETWEEN **FATHER CHRISTMAS** AND **EVE SISULU?**

I GIVE UP.

THEY BOTH ONLY WORK ABOUT **ONE** DAY A YEAR.

HAHA! HAHA! HAHA! HEE-HEE! HEE-HEE! HEE HEE!

HEE HEE!

I HEREBY PROCLAIM THE SILLY SEASON OFFICIALLY _OVER._

HEY!! WHAT ARE YOU READING?!

AN ARTICLE ABOUT "STARTING FRESH IN THE NEW YEAR."

"STEP ONE: FOR A FRESH START, GET RID OF ALL THOSE ANNOYING LITTLE **IRRITATIONS** IN YOUR LIFE."

SLAM!!

I BLAME THE PRESS FOR THIS.

HAVE YOU HEARD ABOUT YOUR MOTHER'S NEW YEAR'S RESOLUTION? SHE WANTS TO "STAY **AS FAR AWAY** FROM GIN & TONICS AS POSSIBLE!"

REALLY?

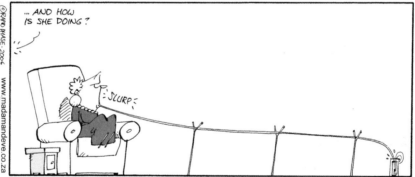

...AND HOW IS SHE DOING?

SLURP

...A SHOT OF **WHISKEY?**

YOUR MOTHER'S GIVEN UP **GIN & TONICS** AS A **NEW YEAR'S RESOLUTION.**

HERE YOU GO. WOULD YOU LIKE TO FOLLOW THAT WITH A **CHASER?**

DON'T MIND IF I DO.

ANY **MORE** NEW YEAR'S RESOLUTIONS?

I'MTH GOOENK THOGED MITHEETH IXED.

HUH?

I'MTH GOOINK TOGETMI-THEETH IXED!

HOLDTH ONTH.

I'M GOING TO GET MY **TEETH** FIXED.

I'VE MADE A NEW YEAR'S RESOLUTION: FROM NOW ON I AM GIVING UP LYING ON THE IRONING BOARD ON MY <u>BACK</u>.

<u>THIS</u> I'VE GOT TO SEE!

TALK ABOUT A "LOOP-HOLE."

IT'S A LITTLE STRANGE... BUT I'LL GET USED TO IT.

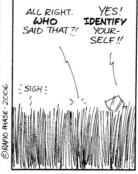

: SIGH :

LOOK OUT!! ELEPHANT STAMPEDE!!

I— IT'S A MIRACLE! THE ELEPHANTS HAVE TRAMPLED THE GRASS INTO A NICE MANAGABLE BACKYARD LAWN!!

FANTASISE ALL YOU WANT, MADAM. THAT'S JUST **NOT** GOING TO HAPPEN.

I WANT MY GARDENER BACK FROM HOLIDAY!!

www.madamandeve.co.za ©RAPID PHASE - 2006

MIELLLIES!!

www.madamandeve.co.za ©RAPID PHASE - 2006

DOES ANYONE HAVE **ANY IDEA** WHEN THE GARDENER'S COMING BACK?!

HEE-HEE.

THAT MUST BE MOM. SHE WENT NEXT DOOR TO SEE IF WE COULD **BORROW** THE **NEIGHBOUR'S** GARDENER.

RUSTLE RUSTLE

www.madamandeve.co.za

FORGET IT! **THEIR** GARDENER HAS BEEN AWAY ON HOLIDAY EVEN **LONGER** THAN OURS!

©RAPID PHASE - 2006

HOW DO YOU KNOW?

Squeak.
Squeak.
Squeak.
..CLICK..

YOU HAVE TO ADMIT EVE'S GETTING MORE PROFESSIONAL.

OH GREAT-- WE'VE LOST GWEN AND EVE! I HATE THESE CROWDED **FLEA MARKETS!!**

DON'T MOVE! MAYBE THEY'RE IN THE NEXT AISLE!!

...SEE THEM?

I'LL TAKE **THAT** ONE.

MADAM & EVE

BY STEPHEN FRANCIS & RICO

Panel 1:

AND IN TODAY'S NEWS -- DEPUTY PRESIDENT PHUMZILE MLAMBO-NGCUKA HAS BEEN SLAMMED BY CRITICS FOR USING A **PRESIDENTIAL JET** TO FLY HER AND HER FAMILY ON A CHRISTMAS HOLIDAY IN THE UNITED ARAB EMIRATES.

Panel 2:

... "THE GRAVY PLANE."

Panel 3:

HELLO,... AND THANK YOU FOR CHOOSING TO FLY **GRAVY PLANE AIRWAYS** -- PAID FOR ENTIRELY BY THE SOUTH AFRICAN TAXPAYERS.

Panel 4:

I'M SURE THE DEPUTY PRESIDENT AND HER FAMILY ARE ANXIOUS TO TAKE OFF, BUT FIRST WE'D LIKE TO AQUAINT YOU WITH SOME OF OUR SAFETY PROCEDURES...

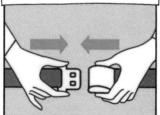

Panel 5:

FOR YOUR SECURITY, BODYGUARDS HAVE BEEN CONVENIENTLY POSITIONED THROUGHOUT THE CABIN. HERE ... HERE ... AND HERE.

Panel 6:

IN THE UNLIKELY EVENT THAT THE BIASED **MEDIA** OR THE **DEMOCRATIC PARTY** CATCH WIND OF THIS FLIGHT, THE CAPTAIN WILL ISSUE THE **BRACE COMMAND.**

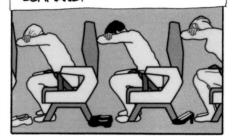

Panel 7:

AT THAT POINT, **DISGUISE MASKS** WILL DROP FROM THE CEILING. SIMPLY PUT THEM ON AND ACT NORMAL.

Panel 8:

SINCE OUR FLIGHT IS PARTIALLY OVER WATER, WHEN WE LAND, ALL PASSENGERS WILL DISEMBARK ON THE GIANT **RUBBER SLIDE.**

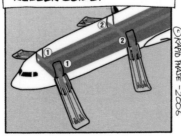

©RAPID PHATE - 2006

Panel 9:

THIS HAS NOTHING TO DO WITH SAFETY... WE JUST THOUGHT THE DEPUTY PRESIDENT'S CHILDREN WOULD REALLY ENJOY IT.

Panel 10:

... AND NOW, FOR TONIGHT'S IN-FLIGHT MOVIE: "LAWRENCE OF ARABIA"...

...**TOLD** YOU WE SHOULD HAVE FLOWN SOUTH AFRICAN AIRWAYS.

AND IN OTHER NEWS, IT HAS COME TO LIGHT THAT SEVERAL OTHER OFFICIALS HAVE ALSO USED THE GOVERNMENT JET FOR PERSONAL USE.

www.madamandeve.co.za © RAPID PHASE · 2006

HMPH. FIRST GRAVY **TRAINS**, NOW GRAVY **PLANES**! WHAT NEXT, I ASK YOU?!

GRAVY STAINS.

SLAM!

POLITICS IS SUCH A CONVERSATION-KILLER THESE DAYS.

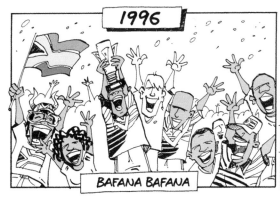

1996

BAFANA BAFANA

www.madamandeve.co.za

2006

YOU SUCK!

BOOFANA BOOFANA

79

MADAM & EVE

BY STEPHEN FRANCIS & RICO

LOCAL GOVT. ELECTIONS
POLLING STATION

ARE YOU **SURE** THIS IS **YOU**? THIS I.D. PHOTO DOESN'T LOOK LIKE YOU AT ALL.

OK, GO ON THROUGH.

SIGH

SIGH

SIGH SIGH SIGH SIGH

RATTLE

BANG! BANG! BANG!

AHEM.

ONLY **ONE** PERSON PER VOTING BOOTH, PLEASE...

...MISTER <u>ZUMA</u>.

SORRY.

MADAM & Eve

BY STEPHEN FRANCIS & RICO

ON THE TWELFTH DAY OF CHRISTMAS, MY TRUE LOVE GAVE TO ME...

TWELVE SCORPIONS CIRCLING

ELEVEN FORGERS FORGING

Nelson Mandela

TEN CHOPPERS CHOPPING

NINE BODS A-GUARDING

EIGHT HURRICANES BLOWING

SEVEN STRIKERS STRIKING

SIX EMPTY PUMPS

FIVE GOL-DEN DEALS

FOUR MP'S CROSSING

THREE FRENCH RIOTS

TWO BUSHES PLOTTING

... AND A PARTRIDGE WAY UP A PEAR TREE!

HAPPY HOLIDAYS FROM MADAM & EVE!!

MADAM & EVE'S CHRISTMAS SHOPPING TIPS.

NEVER LEAVE YOUR BAGS UNATTENDED IN THE CAR.

BUY ALL YOUR CHRISTMAS WRAPPING PAPER THE YEAR BEFORE... AT HALF PRICE!

50% OFF

AVOID TOUCHING ANY FATHER CHRISTMAS MALL DISPLAYS

HELP!! GET HIM OFF ME!!

GOOD MORNING, MADAM. MERRY CHRISTMAS.

CLICK

...AND IN TODAY'S NEWS... PANDEMONIUM REIGNS WORLD-WIDE TODAY AS MILLIONS OF PEOPLE DID **NOT** RECEIVE **CHRISTMAS PRESENTS.** <u>WHY</u> FATHER CHRISTMAS DIDN'T MAKE HIS ROUNDS LAST NIGHT, IS ANYONE'S GUESS...

SNORE SNORE

...WHY I HATE NEW YEARS EVE PARTIES.

OW!!

WHY I **DOUBLEY** HATE NEW YEARS EVE PARTIES.

...C...COFFEE.

WHERE'S EVE?

SHE'S TAKING AN **EXTREME** TEA BREAK.

WHAT'S SO "**EXTREME**" ABOUT IT?

Three HOURS AND counting.

BONK!

THE BODY CORPORATE

MIELLLIES!!

ADVERTISING MANAGER

DIRECTOR OF HUMAN RESOURCES

VICE PRESIDENT

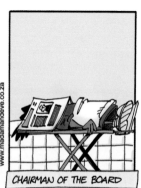

CHAIRMAN OF THE BOARD

Madam & Eve's Art *Appreciation*

Studies in Still Life

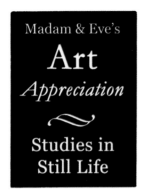

· THE LAST SUPPER ·

www.madamandeve.co.za

LOOK WHAT I BOUGHT AT THE **FLEA MARKET**, EVE. HAND-PAINTED WOODEN FRUIT.

IT LOOKS SO **REALISTIC**! I'LL PUT IT IN THE DINING ROOM.

86

LOOK AT THIS.

YOU EVER WONDER HOW THESE TRAFFIC SIGNS **GET** LIKE THIS?

BEATS ME.

DRESS WARMLY. IT'S **FREEZING** OUTSIDE.

HOW DO YOU KNOW?

M--M--M--M--MIELLIES!!

I'LL GET MY COAT.

© RICO HAAS - 2006

AAAAAAH!! WHAT'S THAT ON MY WINDSCREEN?!

SNIP SNIP SNIP SNIP

3 GUYS ON A BAKKIE Hair Salon

© RICO HAAS - 2006

87

THEY LIVE... IN A PLACE... WITHOUT HOPE.

BUT IN ONE MOMENT...THEIR LIVES WILL CHANGE FOREVER.

OKAY! SO YOU HIJACKED A CAR WITH ME IN IT! NOW WHAT?! I'M HUNGRY! YOU GOT ANY CHEESEBURGERS?!

Gogo TSotsis

Coming Soon to a Cinema near you.

THAT'S ODD. EVE'S BEEN CLEANING THE OVEN FOR HOURS.

...EVE?

LOOK -- THE OLD "STUFFED UNIFORM AND SHOES FAKE MAID CLEANING OVEN TRICK"... AND WE FELL FOR IT!

RIGHT!! YOU'VE GOT SOME EXPLAINING TO DO!!

YOU HAVE TO ADMIT...SHE'S GETTING PRETTY GOOD AT THIS.

THE HEIMLICH MANOEUVRE

WHEEZE CHOKE!! COUGH!!

PTOO!

THE JOBURG MANOEUVRE

WHEEZE CHOKE!!

PTOO!

HEY!! WHERE'S MY WALLET?!

Bishop to Rook 3. Checkmate.

LOOK LIKE THE **COMPUTER** BEAT YOU AT **CHESS** AGAIN.

YA-HAA!!

... BUT WHEN IT COMES TO **KICKBOXING**, IT CAN'T TOUCH ME.

www.madamandeve.co.za

THE FLYING SISULUS.

www.madamandeve.co.za

© RAPID PHASE - 2005

WHERE'S EVE?

IN THE LOUNGE. SHE SAID SOMETHING ABOUT DUSTING THE **CHANDELIER.**

SLAM!

© RAPID PHASE - 2006

www.madamandeve.co.za

SLAM!!

SOME PEOPLE JUST DON'T APPRECIATE A CHANGE OF SEASON.

PIKI TUP

MESSI TUP

SUCKI TUP

DRINKI TUP

NELSON MANDELA Bridge ➡

OR TAMBO Airport ✈ ➡

JACOB ZUMA Courthouse ⬆

AND IN OTHER NEWS... CONCERNING THE ONGOING POWER BLACKOUTS, **ESKOM** SAYS "THERE'S A LIGHT AT THE END OF THE TUNNEL."

NOW IF THEY COULD ONLY GET THE LIGHT TO JUST GO ON ...

LET'S JUST SAY MY MAID MARCHES TO A DIFFERENT DRUMMER.

EVE, DO YOU **HAVE** TO WALK AROUND LIKE THE WHOLE **WORLD'S** ON YOUR SHOULDERS? CAN'T YOU PUT ON A **HAPPY FACE** JUST <u>ONCE</u> IN A WHILE?

SMP
SMP
SMP

www.madamandeve.co.za

MIND IF I LOOK AT A SECTION OF THE PAPER?

UH...

I LOVE THE **SUNDAY TIMES** -- IT'S SO COMPREHENSIVE AND HEAVY..

THERE'S JUST SO MANY SECTIONS...SUPPLEMENTS, AND... UH, ...

©RAPID PHASE - 2006

SPECIAL EDITION.

The Seven Habits of Highly effective Gogos

by Thandi Sisulu

1. They drink.

glug
glug
glug
glug

2. They sleep.

Snore
Snore
Snore
Snore

SLAM!!

LET ME BACK IN! I'M ONLY UP TO NUMBER 3!!

©RAPID PHASE - 2006

www.madamandeve.co.za

"SCRATCH"
"SCRATCH"
"SCRATCH"
"SCRATCH"

EVE!!

©RAPID PHASE - 2006

HERE. PUT THIS **BACK SCRATCHER** BACK. I'M DONE USING IT.

YOU LEARN SOMETHING NEW EVERY DAY -- I'VE ALWAYS THOUGHT THIS WAS A **SALAD FORK**.

www.madamandeve.co.za

YOU KNOW WHAT THEY SAY: "THE GRASS IS ALWAYS GREENER ON THE OTHER SIDE OF THE FENCE."

...AND IF SO, IT'S TIME TO **CHANGE GARDENERS!**

HA HA! HEEHEE!
HAHA! HEEHEE!
HAHA! HEEHEE!

©RAPID PHASE - 2006

www.madamandeve.co.za

MADAM HUMOUR. YOU EITHER GET IT OR YOU DON'T.

95

CAN YOU TELL THE DIFFERENCE? I MADE **ESPRESSO** THIS MORNING.

POP!! AAAH!!

WARNING! WARNING! A virus penetrated your firewall.

FREEZE! Put your hands up! Stop or I'll shoot! Blam! Blam!

Virus terminated. Have a nice day.

"ARMED RESPONSE INTERNET SECURITY."

FOOD CITY

BOTTLE CITY

GARDEN CITY

EVE'S REACHED HER **CITY** LIMITS.

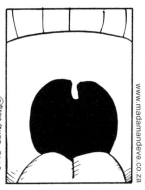

MADAM & Eve

BY STEPHEN FRANCIS & RICO

...AND WE NOW CROSS LIVE TO THE BAFANA BAFANA POST AFRICAN NATIONS CUP PRESS CONFERENCE...

EISH. WHAT CAN WE SAY? WE LOST.

"EISH?"

"EISH?!" THAT'S IT?! AFTER DASHING OUR HOPES... NOT WINNING A SINGLE GAME... NOT EVEN SCORING ONE GOAL?!! -- ALL THEY CAN SAY IS..."EISH?!"

AND IN OTHER NEWS, IT'S NOW EMERGING THAT EVEN **MORE** PARLIAMENTARIANS HAVE BEEN TAKING PART IN THE **TRAVELGATE** SCAM.

WHEN ASKED TO COMMENT, A PRESIDENTIAL SPOKESMAN SAID: "EISH."

AGAIN "EISH?!"

IT'S A SOUTH AFRICAN THING.

SOMETIMES "EISH" IS JUST THE BEST WAY TO EXPRESS HOW YOU FEEL.

© RAPID PHASE 2006

BY THE WAY. WE'RE OUT OF GIN.

@#*#@ EISH!!

NEEDS WORK.

AND IN OTHER NEWS, LOCAL PROGRAMME **FEAR FACTOR SA** GOT OFF TO A SHAKY START... WHEN ONE OF THE CONTESTANTS WAS INJURED IN ONE OF THE FIRST EPISODES. A SPOKESMAN FOR eTV HAD **THIS** TO SAY.

AHEM. WHILE WE AT eTV AND FEAR FACTOR BELIEVE IN TOP NOTCH REALITY TELEVISION, THE SAFETY OF OUR PEOPLE WILL ALWAYS COME FIRST.

THEREFORE, WE PLEDGE TO ENSURE THAT—— OOOPS!!

HELP!! GET THIS PODIUM OFF ME!! **CRASH!!** WATCH OUT FOR THOSE SPOTLIGHTS!!

www.madamandeve.co.za
©RAPID PHASE - 2006

FEAR FACTOR SOUTH AFRICA ON e

www.madamandeve.co.za
©RAPID PHASE - 2006

PLEASE BE PATIENT. WE ARE EXPERIENCING TECHNICAL DIFFICULTIES.

AND NOW...TONIGHT ON **FEAR FACTOR SA**... CONTESTANTS WILL HAVE TO EAT THESE: LARGE **ANIMAL TESTICLES** FROM TWO DIFFERENT ANIMALS!

WATCH OUT! YOU'RE TILTING THE PLATE! :BONK: :BONK: :BONK:

OOPS! I SLIPPED ON A **TESTICLE!!**

CRASH! OW!! IT'S AMAZING HOW ACCIDENT-PRONE THIS SHOW IS.

www.madamandeve.co.za
©RAPID PHASE - 2006

They joined a local reality TV show for fun...

But then... Accidents began to happen.

OW! OW! OW! OW!

-BONK!-BONK!-BONK!

NOW.
They're trying to stay in the game... and stay Alive.

FEAR FACTOR SURVIVOR

A new reality TV show coming soon to a channel near you.

RIGHT! AT THIS **ROAD-BLOCK** THERE'S A HIDDEN **CLUE** FOR YOUR NEXT DESTINATION.! TRY AND FIND IT! READY? **GO**!!

WHOAH!! STOP!! SORRY, BUT YOUR TIME'S UP! YOU'RE **ELIMINATED**!!

HEY! THIS SHOW IS **RIGGED**! WE'RE LODGING A **COMPLAINT**!

...IT'S BECAUSE WE'RE **BLACK**... ISN'T IT?!

THE AMAZING RACE CARD

Coming Soon to a TV Channel near you

104

OPEN UP!! INTERNATIONAL CARTOON POLICE!!

KNOCK! KNOCK!

WE'RE HERE TO ENSURE YOUR CARTOONS ADHERE TO INTERNATIONAL STANDARDS AND <u>DON'T</u> OFFEND, INCITE OR OUTRAGE RELIGIOUS SENSIBILITIES.

NO PROBLEM, OFFICER. THIS IS A FAMILY CARTOON. NOTHING OFFENSIVE OR OUTRAGEOUS <u>HERE</u>.

QUICK. HIDE MOM.

ON IT.

SO. YOU'RE FROM THE "INTERNATIONAL CARTOON POLICE," HUH?

GO AHEAD. FEEL FREE TO LOOK AROUND! NOBODY IN THIS CARTOON IS EVEN **REMOTELY** OFFENSIVE!

ARE THESE GIN & TONICS?

CRASH!

SNIFF! SNIFF!

IS THERE A **REASON** WHY YOUR MAID IS STUFFING THAT ELDERLY LADY INTO THE CUPBOARD?

WHAT CUPBOARD?

THE WHOLE CARTOONING LANDSCAPE HAS CHANGED. WE HAVE CERTAIN STANDARDS TO UPHOLD NOW.

... ANYTHING WE **SAY** OR **DO** ... COULD CAUSE A **WORLDWIDE FURORE.** IT'S A BIG RESPONSIBILITY.

YOU DON'T THINK WE'RE BEING **TOO** CONSERVATIVE, MADAM? ...**TOO** CAREFUL?

HOW DO YOU MEAN?

WELL, GAGGING YOUR MOTHER, FOR EXAMPLE.

BETTER TO BE SAFE THAN SORRY.

THEY SAY IT MIGHT RAIN.

YEBO.

I CAN'T TAKE THIS ANY LONGER! ALL **WEEK** WE'VE BEEN WALKING ON **EGGSHELLS**... WORRYING ABOUT EVEN THE **POSSIBILITY** OF OFFENDING SOMEONE!!

WELL, **I** SAY IT'S TIME TO JUST... BE **OURSELVES**! **DO** WHAT WE WANT TO DO ... AND **SAY** WHAT WE **WANT** TO **SAY**!!

HEAR! HEAR!

www.madamandeve.co.za

WHERE'S YOUR MOTHER?

⁓CHOKE⁓ SHE'S BEEN **SUSPENDED** INDEFINITELY.

www.madamandeve.co.za

SUSPENDED?! BY WHO?

BY THE **INTERNATIONAL CARTOON POLICE.** THEY FOUND HER TOO OUTRAGEOUS AND OFFENSIVE FOR THESE POLITICALLY SENSITIVE TIMES.

BUT... WHERE **IS** SHE? WHERE DID THEY **TAKE** HER?

⁓SOB⁓ TO A... CARTOON CAMP.

CARTOON CAMP

SO. WHAT ARE YOU IN FOR?

MADAM & EVE

BY STEPHEN FRANCIS & RICO

AND IN OTHER NEWS,...THE WHITE HOUSE SAID THEY WILL ISSUE A STATEMENT SOON ON THE INTERNATIONAL CARTOON CONTROVERSY.

NEVER MIND THOSE CARTOONS. WE'VE GOT BIGGER PROBLEMS.

TAKE A LOOK AT THIS.

CLICK!

...OR THIS.

CLICK!

WAR PLANS

I MEAN, DOES THAT LOOK LIKE ME?!

UH NO, SIR. YOUR EARS ARE MUCH SMALLER.

WE'RE SITTING ON A TIME BOMB! IF THE AMERICAN PEOPLE SEE THESE IMAGES OF ME...THERE'S NO TELLING HOW THEY WILL REACT!

BURNING! PILLAGING! LOOTING! THE OUTRAGE!! --EVEN I WON'T BE ABLE TO STOP IT!!

UH...SIR?

WHO DREW THIS ANYWAY?

WITH APOLOGIES TO ZAPIRO

SOME GUY... CALLS HIMSELF "ZAPIRO."

SOUNDS RUSSIAN. BETTER HAVE THE CIA PICK HIM UP FOR HIS OWN PROTECTION. PUT HIM IN ONE OF THE "CARTOONIST CAMPS."

UH, SIR? DID YOU SAY... "CARTOONIST CAMPS"?

HEY LOOK -- HE DREW ME WITH A COWBOY HAT.

© RICO PRAIE - 2006

CLICK!

MADAM & EVE

BY STEPHEN FRANCIS & RICO

AND NOW... STAY TUNED FOR... "ISIDINGO!"

YAWN!

≈ Click ≈

..."DAYS OF OUR LIVES."
≈ CLICK ≈
..."THE BOLD AND THE BEAUTIFUL."
≈ CLICK ≈
..."BACKSTAGE."
≈ CLICK ≈
≈ CLICK ≈
≈ CLICK ≈
≈ CLICK ≈

...IN ALL MY YEARS... I'VE NEVER **SEEN** SUCH DESPICABLE BEHAVIOUR.

AH. FINALLY.

WHERE DOES IT END?! THE **GREED**! THE **MANIPULATION**!

--THE WANTON SEX--

-- HOW **DARE** YOU?! **NO ONE** CAN **JUDGE** ME -- ESPECIALLY NOT _YOU_!!

W-WHAT ARE YOU **SAYING**?!

...YOU **REALLY** WANT TO **KNOW**?!

YES! YES!

YEARS AGO... I FATHERED A SON -- WITH YOUR **SISTER**!

≈GASP≈   ≈GASP≈

YOU MEAN--

YES! I AM THE SECRET FATHER OF YOUR OWN NEPHEW!!

© RAPID PHASE · 2006

WHAT ARE YOU WATCHING? ..."SCANDAL?" ..."GENERATIONS?"

... ZUMA RAPE TRIAL.

LUKE...
I AM YOUR
FATHER.

STAR WARS

JUDGE... I AM
YOUR NEPHEW'S
FATHER!

ZUMA WARS

THE ZUMA TRIAL...

YOU MEAN..

YES, JUDGE!
I AM THE
FATHER OF MY
LOVE CHILD...
WHOSE SECRET
IDENTITY IS --
YOUR NEPHEW!!

...THE VERY SAME
"LOVE CHILD NEPHEW"...
WHO, WHEN HE GREW
TO MANHOOD, WAS
CHARGED WITH THE VERY
SAME CRIME AS I
AM NOW!

...YOU
FOLLOWING
THIS?

SEE IF
THERE'S
SOMETHING
ELSE ON...
SIMPLER
AND LESS
COMPLICATED.

AND WE'LL BE
BACK WITH MORE
"GENERATIONS"
... AFTER THIS.

Click!

OKAY, CLASS! YOUR
BIOLOGY TEST IS IN
FRONT OF YOU.
YOU HAVE 30 MINUTES.
READY? BEGIN.

QUESTION ONE:
"WHERE DO BABIES
COME FROM?"

JACOB ZUMA.

THIS IS THE BIG MOMENT! EVERYTHING ELSE FITS! NOW... LET'S SEE .... IF THE DNA TEST MATCHES!

© RAPID PHASE - 2006

OH, NO!! IT'S A NEGATIVE!!

:GASP:

I'M SORRY. IT WAS A CLOSE CALL... BUT YOU'VE BEEN ELIMINATED!

B--BUT-- LOOK! I HAVE HIS EYES!

AND WE'LL BE BACK WITH MORE OF... "ZUMA LOVE CHILD SURVIVOR". AFTER THIS.

THESE REALITY SHOWS WORK FAST.

www.madamandeve.co.za

I DIDN'T KNOW THE CIRCUS WAS IN TOWN...

POLICE

© RAPID PHASE - 2006

www.madamandeve.co.za

ZUMA TRIAL.

POLICE

AND IN OTHER NEWS... THERE WAS ANOTHER POWER BLACKOUT THROUGHOUT MOST OF THE "MOTHER CITY" TODAY...

IF CAPE TOWN IS THE "MOTHER CITY"... DOES THAT MEAN JOBURG IS THE "FATHER CITY"?

© RAPID PHASE - 2006

www.madamandeve.co.za

ASK JACOB ZUMA.

MOM!!

AND WITH LOCAL ELECTION RESULTS NOW **IN** -- THE **ANC** HAS COME **FIRST** ... WITH THE **DA** COMING IN SECOND...

AND IN A SURPRISE TURN -- **ONE THIRD** OF VOTERS VOTED FOR "**MISTER DELIVERY**."

... ORDERING "NEW HOUSING", "LOWER RATES", "BETTER EMPLOYMENT" AND "LOWER CRIME."

HOW LONG DOES MISTER DELIVERY TAKE TO DELIVER?

ABOUT FORTY-FIVE MINUTES. ...WHY?

ALL THOSE WHO **VOTED**, PUT UP YOUR HANDS.

WHAT DO YOU THINK? OF **COURSE** WE VOTED! WE'VE BEEN FOLLOWING THINGS FROM THE VERY BEGINNING!

OKAY, JUST WANTED TO MAKE SURE YOU VOTED.

AND NOW, BACK TO **IDOLS**.

DID YOU VOTE FOR THE FIRST OR THE SECOND FINALIST?

FIRST.

UNBELIEVABLE. THE **ANC** HAS CLAIMED **ANOTHER** SIGNIFICANT ELECTION VICTORY!

I DON'T GET IT.

HOW CAN YOU KEEP VOTING THE **SAME PEOPLE** INTO OFFICE WHEN THEY DON'T DELIVER THE GOODS?!

I DON'T KNOW EITHER, SIR.

MADAM & Eve

BY STEPHEN FRANCIS & RICO

KLIPPITY-KLOP! KLIPPITY-KLOP!!

BE DARK SOON. WE BETTER MAKE CAMP.

AH. THIS IS THE LIFE. NOTHING BUT THE WIDE OPEN PLAINS... SHEEP... A ROARING FIRE... AND THE STARS OVER OUR HEADS.

YOU KNOW, EVE...

...DID I EVER TELL YOU HOW MUCH I LIKE YOU?

BROKEBACK MADAM

Coming Soon to a Cinema near you.

CAN YOU LEND ME FIVE BUCKS? I NEED IT FOR SCHOOL.

I JUST **LENT** YOU FIVE BUCKS **HALF AN HOUR** AGO!!

DID YOU? SORRY, ... I MUST HAVE HAD A **BLACKOUT**.

SLAM!!

ESKOM SEEMS TO GET AWAY WITH IT...

www.madamandeve.co.za

AND, IN OTHER NEWS, PUBLIC ENTERPRISE'S MINISTER ALEC ERWIN HAS BLAMED THE **ESKOM BLACKOUTS** ON A MYSTERIOUS <u>LOOSE BOLT</u>.

www.madamandeve.co.za

RIDICULOUS. AS IF A MYSTERIOUS "LOOSE BOLT" CAUSED ALL THIS TROUBLE!

© RAPID PHASE - 2006

BONK!

OW!!

WHERE AM I? **WHO** AM I?

© RAPID PHASE - 2006

AND IN OTHER NEWS... JACOB ZUMA CLAIMS HE'S **NOT RESPONSIBLE** FOR HIS ACTIONS... AS HE'S A VICTIM OF HIS LOOSE BOLT.

© RAPID PHASE - 2006

www.madamandeve.co.za

UH... THAT IS TO SAY... HE'S NOT RESPONSIBLE FOR HIS ACTIONS... AS HE WAS **HIT** BY A LOOSE BOLT.

OHHHH.

OKAY, CLASS. PLEASE HAND YOUR EXERCISE BOOKS TO THE FRONT-- YES, THANDI?

I WAS UNABLE TO FINISH MY HOMEWORK ASSIGNMENT.

AND WHY IS THAT?

I WAS HIT BY A MYSTERIOUS **LOOSE BOLT** AND BLACKED OUT.

PRINCIPAL

THANKS A **LOT**, ESKOM.

AND WE'LL BE BACK WITH **MORE** OF OUR INVESTIGATIVE PROGRAMME: "LOOSE BOLTS... THE HIDDEN MENACE"...

BUT FIRST, ...A WORD FROM OUR SPONSOR, **ESKOM**.

LOOSE BOLTS... LOOSE BOLTS... I'M SO SICK OF EVERYONE BLAMING EVERYTHING ON LOOSE BOLTS!

CRASH!

Panel 1: HOW'S THE **TRIAL** GOING, JACOB?

UH... FINE, MISTER PRESIDENT. WE'RE HOPING FOR A BRIEF POSTPONEMENT.

Panel 2: GREAT! I WAS THINKING YOU **NEED** TO TAKE SOME TIME OFF! I PULLED A FEW STRINGS... AND GOT YOU AN ALL-EXPENSE PAID TRIP TO **AMERICA!**

...REALLY, THABO?

Panel 3: SURE! I'VE DONE YOUR WHOLE ITINERARY! ...BORROW MY JET! ...FLY FIRST CLASS TO WASHINGTON D.C.! ...MEET WITH PRESIDENT GEORGE W. BUSH!

Panel 4: ...GO ON A **HUNTING TRIP** WITH VICE-PRESIDENT DICK CHENEY...

HOLD IT.

Panel 5: AND, IN OTHER NEWS... IN AN EFFORT TO AVOID ADVERSE TRIAL PUBLICITY, **PRESIDENT MBEKI** HAS SENT **JACOB ZUMA** ON A TRIP TO AMERICA... IN ORDER TO GO **HUNTING** WITH VICE PRESIDENT **DICK CHENEY.**

Panel 6: TENNESSEE, USA

YEP. I **LOVE** THE GREAT OUTDOORS. YOU EVER GO QUAIL HUNTING IN AFRICA, JACOB?

NOT REALLY, DICK.

Panel 7: UH...DICK? YOUR SHOTGUN'S RESTING AGAINST MY HEAD AGAIN.

Panel 8: OOPS. DANG. ...SORRY, FORCE OF HABIT.

IF I SURVIVE... I'LL **GET** THABO FOR THIS.

Panel 9: HUNTING QUAIL ...WITH DICK CHENEY & JACOB ZUMA

YOU'RE NOT NERVOUS ARE YOU, JACOB? ...CONSIDERING I **SHOT** MY LAST HUNTING PARTNER.

UH...NOPE.

Panel 10: -- BECAUSE YOU DON'T HAVE TO BE NERVOUS. WE MAY BE OUT IN THE MIDDLE OF **NOWHERE** -- BUT I AIN'T GONNA SHOOT YOU.

WHEW

Panel 11:

Panel 12: ...YOU EVER SEE THAT MOVIE "BROKEBACK MOUNTAIN"?

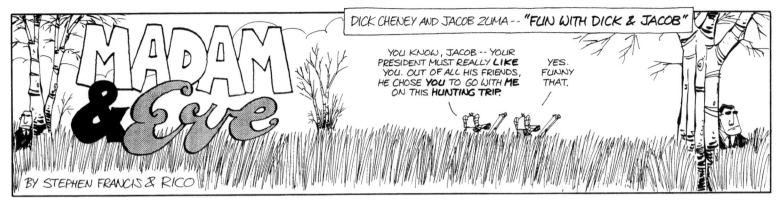

MADAM & Eve

BY STEPHEN FRANCIS & RICO

DICK CHENEY AND JACOB ZUMA -- "FUN WITH DICK & JACOB"

YOU KNOW, JACOB -- YOUR PRESIDENT MUST REALLY **LIKE** YOU. OUT OF ALL HIS FRIENDS, HE CHOSE **YOU** TO GO WITH **ME** ON THIS **HUNTING TRIP**.

YES. FUNNY THAT.

UH... MAYBE WE SHOULD SWITCH POSITION.

WHOA... JACOB! DON'T TELL ME YOU'RE **NERVOUS** BECAUSE I **SHOT** MY LAST HUNTING PARTNER?!

WELL... ACTUALLY...

OH COME ON! THAT WAS TOTALLY **DIFFERENT.**

...IT WAS A **CONSENSUAL** SHOOTING.

HUH?

OH YEAH. HE **WANTED** ME TO SHOOT HIM.

UH... HOW COULD YOU TELL, DICK?

©RAPID PHASE · 2006

IT WAS <u>SO</u> OBVIOUS! HIS WHOLE **ATTITUDE!** THE WAY HE WAS **DRESSED!** HE WAS PRACTICALLY **BEGGING** TO BE SHOT!!

I'LL SHOW YOU WHAT I MEAN ... <u>LOOK</u> AT ME.

OH YEAH. **YOU** WANT IT TOO, ALL RIGHT.

HELP!! SECRET SERVICE!!

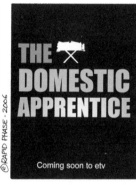

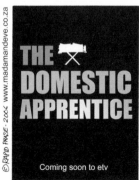

THE DOMESTIC APPRENTICE

Coming soon to etv

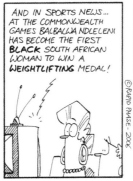

HAPPY BIRTHDAY TO YOU... HAPPY BIRTHDAY TO YOU... HAPPY BIRTHDAY MISTER PRESIDENT...

WAIT A DANG MINUTE! IT'S NOT MY BIRTHDAY!

WE KNOW, SIR. ...IT'S THE GULF WAR'S BIRTHDAY.

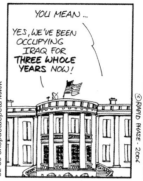

YOU MEAN...

YES, WE'VE BEEN OCCUPYING IRAQ FOR THREE WHOLE YEARS NOW!

SIGH: TIME SURE FLIES WHEN YOU'RE HAVING FUN.

SHOULD AULD AQUAINTANCE BE FORGOT...

I CAN'T BELIEVE IT, MISTER PRESIDENT, THE IRAQ WAR IS THREE YEARS OLD TODAY.

YEP.

WE SHOULD CELEBRATE, SIR.

WELL,...CALL ME NOSTALGIC... BUT I'VE BEEN KEEPING A IRAQ WAR SCRAPBOOK.

A SCRAP-BOOK, SIR?

CHECK IT OUT. PAGE ONE: THE ORIGINAL INVASION ORDER... SIGNED BY ME.

AND LOOK HERE! ...OUR VERY FIRST DETENTION CENTER!

AWWWWW!!

HAPPY BIRTHDAY TO YOU... HAPPY BIRTHDAY TO YOU... HAPPY BIRTHDAY MISTER RRE-SI-DENT...

...HAPPY 3 YEAR-OLD IRAQI INVASION TO YOUUUU!!

CLAP! CLAP! CLAP!

YOU GUYS! --YOU REALLY DIDN'T HAVE TO DO THIS!!

YEE-HA!!

WHISTLE!

CLAP! CLAP! CLAP!

HOO! HOO! HOO!

OH, NO! : HEE-HEE: NOT A GORILLA-GRAM!!

BOY, THIS IRAQ WAR 3RD BIRTHDAY PARTY IS REALLY SOMETHING! I CAN'T WAIT UNTIL NEXT YEAR!!

THAT'S NOT ALL, MISTER PRESIDENT. WE HAVE A SURPRISE GUEST!

DICK CHENEY! --JUST BACK FROM QUAIL HUNTING!!

YEE-HA!! BLAM!! BLAM!!

HEE-HEE. JUST BLANKS, MISTER PRESIDENT!

YOU GUYS! HELP ME UP.

MIELLIES!!

TODAY'S TOP STORY: WHICH SUBURBAN HOUSEHOLD HAS NOT PAID THEIR GARDENER IN OVER TWO MONTHS?!

THIS IS MLN, MIELIE LADY NEWS --WE'LL BE RIGHT BACK AFTER ANOTHER WORD FROM OUR SPONSOR!!

MIELLIES!!

MADAM & EVE

BY STEPHEN FRANCIS & RICO

AND IN INTERNATIONAL NEWS: U.S. PRESIDENT GEORGE W. BUSH'S APPROVAL RATINGS ARE SO LOW ... THAT MANY POLITICIANS IN HIS OWN PARTY NOW CONSIDER HIM A LIABILITY...

GENTLEMEN, WE NEED A WAR!

UH, SIR... WE'VE ALREADY DONE THAT.

NO. I READ THIS SOMEWHERE: "EVERY GREAT U.S. PRESIDENT HAS HAD: a) A WAR... b) A WAR WHERE THEY WERE ATTACKED."

WHAT ABOUT 9-11, SIR?

DOESN'T COUNT. THAT WASN'T A COUNTRY...EVEN THOUGH WE RESPONDED BY... UH, INVADING IRAQ.

NO. IF I'M GOING TO BE A GREAT PRESIDENT... WE NEED ANOTHER WAR, AND THIS TIME WE NEED TO BE THE ATTACKEE INSTEAD OF THE ATTACKER.

WHAT WE NEED IS A PLAN. A PLAN TO UPSET AND PROVOKE COUNTRIES ALL OVER THE WORLD TO ATTACK US.

INSULT THEIR PRESIDENTS?

NO, SOMETHING WORSE THAN INSULTS... SOMETHING TOTALLY FOOLPROOF...

©RAPID PHASE - 2006

AND IN OTHER NEWS, PRESIDENT BUSH ANNOUNCED HIS NEW PROGRAMME OF "GETTING TO KNOW WORLD LEADERS"... CALLED: "HUNTING WITH DICK CHENEY".

MADAM & EVE

BY STEPHEN FRANCIS & RICO

AND, IN OTHER NEWS... DUE TO THE NUMEROUS **MISTAKES** ALREADY MADE IN THE **ZUMA INVESTIGATION**, THE SOUTH AFRICAN POLICE SERVICE HAS BROUGHT IN A WELL-KNOWN INTERNATIONAL CRIME **EXPERT** TO TAKE OVER THE CASE.

YOU HAVE BEEN EXPECTING ME. MY NAME... IS **INSPECTOR CLOUSEAU.**

RIGHT THIS WAY, INSPECTOR. ...FOLLOW ME.

BONK!

RIGHT. YOU GO TO ZE LEFT. I WILL GO TO ZE RIGHT.

GOOD PLAN, SIR.

BY ZE WAY, I WILL BE NEEDING TISSUE SAMPLES.

WAY AHEAD OF YOU, SIR.

AHA! ZE **GUEST ROOM!** SO... 215 IS WHERE ZE ALLEGED CRIME TOOK PLACE.

UH... WE'RE NOT REALLY **SURE**... EITHER THE **GUEST** ROOM OR THE **BED**ROOM.

RIGHT. BETTER SECURE ZE AREA.

VERY GOOD, SIR.

BONK! CRASH!

AAAAAAH!!

RIIIIP!

INSPECTOR!! ARE YOU <u>OKAY</u>?!

SACRE BLEU. ZESE GUYS MAKE ME LOOK GOOD.

THE NEW PINK PANTHER

Starring the South African Police Service

Coming to a cinema near you

©RAPID PHASE - 2006

127

CLUEDO UPDATED...

COLONEL MUSTARD IN THE BILLIARD ROOM... WITH THE REVOLVER.

MRS WHITE IN THE LOUNGE WITH THE CANDLE STICK.

MRS PEACOCK IN THE KITCHEN WITH A KNIFE.

MR ZUMA IN THE GUEST ROOM WITH THE LEAD PIPE.

MY TURN! I SAY... IT WAS... MISTER ZUMA IN THE GUEST ROOM!

NOT GOOD ENOUGH! YOU NEED TO KNOW THE WEAPON! WHAT WEAPON DID HE USE IN THE GUEST ROOM?!

MORE SOUTH AFRICAN CLUEDO...

PROFESSOR PLUM IN THE STUDY WITH THE REVOLVER.

MRS WHITE IN THE LOUNGE WITH THE PANIC BUTTON.

MR GREEN IN THE GARDEN WITH THE LAWNMOWER.

MS SISULU IN THE LAUNDRY WITH THE ROPE.

128

AND IN OTHER NEWS... THOUSANDS OF THE COUNTRY'S LEAST ROADWORTHY MINIBUS **TAXIS** WILL BE SCRAPPED WITHIN NINE MONTHS.

WE'RE TALKING ABOUT THE ONES THAT ARE OLD, WORN, WITH A WOBBLY CHASSIS AND RUNNING ON FUMES.

WHAT ARE YOU LOOKING AT?

NOTHING.

OH NO!! PLEASE. NOT MY FOOT. DON'T TAKE MY FOOT!!

AAAAAH!! WAIT! NOT MY **HAND**!! NOOOO!!

HELP!...NOT MY **EAR**!! YOU'RE EATING MY **EAR**! NOOOOO!! SOMEBODY **HELP**!!

CHOMP CHOMP CHOCOLATE EASTER BUNNIES... THEY'RE SUCH **FUN** TO EAT.

I DON'T CARE **WHAT** THE HOME AFFAIRS COMPUTER SAYS. I AM **NOT** "PRESENTLY DECEASED."

Teller 6A

© RAPID PHASE · 2006

IT ALSO SAYS THAT YOU HAVE 27 UNPAID PARKING TICKETS.

www.madamandeve.co.za

Teller 6A

YOU'RE RIGHT. I DIED MONTHS AGO. JUST STAMP MY BOOK AND I'LL BE ON MY WAY.

IT'S ALWAYS THE DEAD ONES THAT COMPLAIN THE MOST.

HI MOM. HOW WAS HOME AFFAIRS?

HOW SHOULD **I** KNOW? I'M **DEAD**.

© RAPID PHASE · 2006

THEY STAMPED MY I.D. BOOK ..."**PRESENTLY DECEASED.**"

PRESENTLY DECEASED?! ... WELL, WE'RE GOING TO HAVE TO **DO** SOMETHING ABOUT THIS !!

I'M CALLING OUR BROKER. MAYBE WE CAN COLLECT ON YOUR <u>LIFE</u> <u>INSURANCE</u>.

www.madamandeve.co.za

"PRESENTLY DECEASED?" HI -- I'M "PREVIOUSLY DISADVANTAGED."

NICE TO MEET YOU. I'M CURRENTLY DEHYDRATED.

MADAM & Eve

BY STEPHEN FRANCIS & RICO

GOOD MORNING, MISTER PHELPS...

YOUR MISSION, SHOULD YOU CHOOSE TO ACCEPT IT, IS TO INVESTIGATE AND EXPOSE THE ENTIRE **ANC E-MAIL SPY SAGA**...

...DETERMINE **WHO** IS INVOLVED, WHO IS SPYING ON **WHO**... AND PROVE ONCE AND FOR ALL WHETHER THE INCRIMINATING E-MAILS ARE GENUINE OR PART OF A CONSPIRACY TO IMPLICATE SENIOR ANC LEADERS.

UH... YOU GOT AN **EASIER** MISSION?

: SIGH :

OKAY... YOUR **NEW** MISSION, IF YOU CHOOSE TO ACCEPT IT, IS TO UNRAVEL THE WHOLE **TRUTH** IN THE **ZUMA TRIAL**... DETERMINE **WHO** IS LYING, WHICH **ROOM** THE ALLEGED CRIME TOOK PLACE, AND...

UH... STILL EASIER.

RIGHT... THOUSANDS OF MINIBUS TAXIS IN SOUTH AFRICA ARE UNSAFE AND UNROADWORTHY. YOUR MISSION IS TO...

YOU MUST BE JOKING.

: SIGH :

HEY! I'D LIKE TO GET A COOL DRINK! ARE YOU GOING TO STAND THERE **ALL** DAY?!

MISSION IMPOSSIBLE
SOUTH AFRICA

COMING SOON TO A CINEMA NEAR YOU.

MADAM & EVE

BY STEPHEN FRANCIS & RICO

GO AHEAD, MISTER ZUMA. WE'RE WAITING.

AHEM.

UHUBHUZA AMANGA ALUHLAZA!

UCANSI BELUNGAPHOQIWE, BESIVUMELENE.

NGAVELE NGAMBONA UKUTHI VELE NAYE UYANGIHALELA.

EMVA KWALOKHO NGIYE NGAGEZA.

ABEZINDABA BANGIHLINZELA EZIBINI!

ALUKHO OLUBI ENGILWENZILE.

OH PLEASE. GUILTY, GUILTY, GUILTY.

© RAPID PHASE - 2006

GREAT SOUTH AFRICAN LIES AND MYTHS

"YOUR CHEQUE IS IN THE POST."

"SORRY, I DON'T HAVE ANY CHANGE."

"WE'VE TURNED THE CORNER ON CRIME."

"THE RISK OF HIV CAN BE MINIMISED BY TAKING A SHOWER."

© RAPID PHASE 2006

WHATEVER YOUR PROBLEM... A TOUGH DAY IN COURT... OR A NIGHT OF UNPROTECTED SEX...

THERE'S NOTHING LIKE A SOOTHING HOT SHOWER TO PUT THINGS RIGHT.

AAAAAH.

ABC
Shower & Bathroom Fixtures

© RAPID PHASE 2006

www.madamandeve.co.za

...G#X G*# ADVERTISERS.

SLAM!

© RAPID PHASE 2006

www.madamandeve.co.za

CAN I ASK YOU A QUESTION?

SURE. MAKE IT QUICK.

WHAT'S WRONG WITH TAKING A SHOWER AFTER SEX?

EVE!! WHY DIDN'T YOU WASH THE DISHES?!

YOU MAY **THINK** YOU WANTED ME TO WASH THE DISHES... BUT I KNOW WHAT YOU **REALLY** WANT: YOU WANT ME TO TAKE A **TEA BREAK**.

... SO I TOOK A DECISION **NOT** TO WASH THE DISHES, (WHICH WAS TOTALLY CONSENSUAL ON BOTH OUR PARTS.) IF ANYBODY WANTS ME, I'LL BE TAKING A SHOWER.

ZUMA SPEAK.

EVE! YOU FORGOT TO DO THE VACUUMING!!

NO, I DIDN'T.

THE RUG DOESN'T **WANT** TO BE VACUUMED. WHEN IT DOES, YOU'LL BE THE FIRST TO KNOW.

THE LOUNGE, HOWEVER, IS PRACTICALLY **BEGGING** TO BE DUSTED THIS AFTERNOON.

MEANWHILE, I'LL BE IN THE KITCHEN DOING A BIT OF **CONSENSUAL COOKING**.

I'LL BE REALLY GLAD WHEN THE ZUMA TRIAL IS OVER.

KNOCK! KNOCK!

WHO'S THERE?!

CHUCK NORRIS.

I HATE MONDAYS.

WHY DID CHUCK NORRIS CROSS THE ROAD?

I GIVE UP. ...WHY?

ARE YOU CRAZY?! NOBODY QUESTIONS THE MOTIVES OF CHUCK NORRIS!!

HEEHEE! HAHAHA! HOOHOOHOO!

HEEHEE! HOHOHO! HAHAHA!

I MUST BE MISSING SOMETHING HERE.

YOU MESS WITH THE BULL... YOU GET THE HORNS!

SPINNING ROUNDHOUSE KICK!!

HE-YAH!!

CRASH!

OOPS.

I WONDER WHAT CHUCK NORRIS WOULD DO IN THIS SITUATION.

MADAM & EVE

BY STEPHEN FRANCIS & RICO

CHUCK NORRIS IS HERE TO SEE YOU, MISTER PRESIDENT.

THANK GOODNESS! SEND HIM IN.

--WAIT!! YOU DON'T "SEND" CHUCK NORRIS ANYWHERE! --ASK HIM IF HE'S READY TO COME IN.

YES, SIR.

WAIT!! YOU DON'T "ASK" CHUCK NORRIS ANYTHING! TELL HIM HE CAN SEE ME WHEN HE FEELS LIKE IT.

YES, SIR.

CHUCK!! --HOW'S IT GOING?!!

JUST GREAT, GEORGE.

...I FOUND OSAMA.

WAY TO GO, CHUCK! I KNEW I COULD COUNT ON YOU!!

YEAH. HE'S OUTSIDE IN THE BOOT OF MY CAR. ...WANT ME TO BRING HIM IN?

UH... NOT JUST YET. I HAVE SOME OTHER PROBLEMS I NEED YOU TO DEAL WITH.

...EVER BEEN TO IRAQ, CHUCK?

NO... BUT IRAQ'S BEEN TO ME.

GRAND PHASE · 2006

-- GET DOWN, MISTER PRESIDENT!!

CHUCK! WHAT ARE YOU DOING?!

CRASH!

...WHAT WAS THAT?

YOU DON'T PUT CHUCK NORRIS IN A CARTOON... WITHOUT ASKING HIS PERMISSION.

"Memoirs of a Domestic Worker..."

ABOUT YOUR WAGES...WE EACH WRITE DOWN WHAT WE THINK IS FAIR...THEN WE SWITCH PAPERS...

©RAPID PHASE - 2006

CRASH!!

"Chapter Two: Sometime later... we both regain consciousness..."

www.madamandeve.co.za

"Memoirs of a Domestic Worker"

OH, WHO'S THIS OLD...ER, CHARMING ELDERLY LADY?

THAT'S MY MOTHER, EDITH.

OH NO, DON'T WORRY. SHE LIVES FAR AWAY IN ENGLAND. YOU'LL NEVER HAVE TO TAKE CARE OF HER.

©RAPID PHASE - 2006

www.madamandeve.co.za

"Chapter Three: I am duped."

EVE!! IT'S AFTER FIVE!! WHERE'S MY GIN & TONIC?!

144

MAY I LEAVE THE DISHES IN THE SINK?

...YOU MAY.

MAY I LIE DOWN ON THE IRONING BOARD NOW?

FINE.

MAY I TAKE THE DAY OFF?

≥SIGH≤

I HATE "MAY DAY."

GOOD MORNING, EVE.

SORRY, I'M **LATE** FOR WORK, MADAM. THE **TRAFFIC** WAS HELL.

WHAT TRAFFIC?! EVE LIVES AT THE BACK OF THE HOUSE!

EVE!!

HEY, IT WAS WORTH A SHOT.

MADAM & Eve

BY STEPHEN FRANCIS & RICO

Thank goodness you've come, Doctor! My mother's been acting very strangely.

Mom! The doctor's here.

HONK!!

...You say your mother's been stocking up on gin and tonic?

Yes, she's ordered triple the usual amount... and there's David Beckham posters all over the house!

Hmm. Her blood pressure is elevated. Let me try the stethoscope. Breathe deeply...

...and exhale.

O-LE!! OLE!! OLE!! OLE!!

Well, that tears it. I'm afraid your mother has SOCCER WORLD CUP FEVER.

Is that serious, Doctor?

Well... there IS a lot of it going around this month...

What should I do?

Take two disprins... and for your mother's sake, hope ENGLAND wins.

What about a SECOND OPINION?

Take two disprins and for my sake, hope GERMANY wins.

©RAPID PHASE-2006

HELP!! GET HER OFF ME!!

Hope it's not contagious.

OKAY, TELL ME: **ARE** WE, OR ARE WE **NOT** THE MAJOR **WORLD** POWER?

WE ARE, MISTER PRESIDENT.

AND IF THERE'S A **WORLD** CONFERENCE OR EVENT... ISN'T **AMERICA** THE FIRST TO BE INVITED?

ABSOLUTELY.

AND WHEN IT COMES TO **BASEBALL**... WHERE IS THE **WORLD** SERIES HELD EVERY SINGLE YEAR?!

AMERICA, SIR.

EXACTLY! I WANT A COMPLETE REPORT ON THIS "SOCCER **WORLD** CUP"!! ...**WHERE** IS IT? ...**WHY** AREN'T WE WINNING? ... AND WHAT **SPORT** ARE THEY PLAYING?!

UH...SIR?

UH...PRESIDENT BUSH? I REALLY DON'T THINK THE **SOCCER WORLD CUP** IS A PLOT TO EXCLUDE THE UNITED STATES!

NONSENSE! THE WHOLE THING'S A **CONSPIRACY!** ...AND WHEN I FIND OUT **WHO'S** BEHIND IT...

WELL, SIR -- THAT WOULD BE **FIFA**.

"FIFA", HUH? ...SOUNDS IRANIAN.

UH, SIR...

CALL THE CIA! I WANT THIS **FIFA** PERSON FOUND AND **ARRESTED!**

UH, SIR...

I'M TELLING YOU... HAVING THE "SOCCER WORLD CUP" IN A **FOREIGN** COUNTRY IS AN **INSULT** TO EVERY AMERICAN WHO ISN'T FOREIGN!

BUT PRESIDENT BUSH...

WHY, THAT'S ALMOST LIKE... HOLDING THE **WORLD SERIES** IN A COUNTRY OTHER THAN AMERICA!

CALL THE JOINT CHIEFS. WE'RE INVADING GERMANY.

UH, SIR...?

PRESIDENT BUSH -- ARE YOU SAYING YOU'RE **JEALOUS** ... BECAUSE THE SOCCER WORLD CUP IS **NOT** BEING HELD IN AMERICA.

ABSOLUTELY <u>NOT</u>.

WE AMERICANS CAN AFFORD TO BE GRACIOUS. WE ALREADY **HAVE** MANY IMPORTANT "**WORLD**" EVENTS HERE.

"THE **WORLD** SERIES." ..."THE MISS **WORLD** PAGEANT." ...THAT JAMES BOND FILM, "THE **WORLD** IS NOT ENOUGH."

UH... "ADULT **WORLD**".

MISTER PRESIDENT! MISTER PRESIDENT!

PRESIDENT BUSH... WE'RE TRYING TO TELL YOU, SIR. AMERICA WAS **NOT** EXCLUDED FROM THE SOCCER WORLD CUP.

WE WEREN'T?

NO SIR. THE USA **IS** REPRESENTED. WE HAVE A TEAM OVER THERE NOW.

...WE DO?

YES. UNFORTUNATELY, WE WERE BEATEN BY THE CZECHS.

CHEQUES? **WHAT** CHEQUES?!

YOU EXPLAIN THIS ONE.

DON'T TELL ME THEIR CHEQUES **BOUNCED**?!

WORLD CUP LESSONS

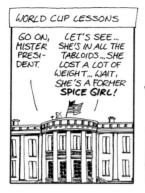

GO ON, MISTER PRESI-DENT.

LET'S SEE... SHE'S IN ALL THE TABLOIDS... SHE LOST A LOT OF WEIGHT... WAIT, SHE'S A FORMER **SPICE GIRL!**

"VICTORIA!" CORRECT, SIR! VERY GOOD! -- AND SHE'S MARRIED TO **DAVID BECKHAM!**

...WHO?!

...MAYBE WE SHOULD START WITH THE **BASICS**.

MISTER PRESIDENT... **THIS**...IS A **SOCCER BALL.**

DO YOU THINK I'M AN **IDIOT?!**

...RONALDO PLAYS A LONG PASS TO ROBERTO CARLOS, HE DRIBBLES PAST TWO DEFENDERS -- AND HE'S FOULED. FREE KICK TO BRAZIL...

THE SHOT IS OVER THE WALL, GOALKEEPER PLETIKOSA SAVES -- THROWS OUT TO IVAN KLASNIC, WHO SETS OFF ON A RUN DOWN THE LEFT FLANK AND...

HERE'S YOUR GIN & TONIC, MOTHER ANDERSON.

AAAAH!!

...MAYBE I **HAVE** BEEN WATCHING **TOO MUCH** WORLD CUP SOCCER.

CHECK IT OUT. THE **LIZARDS** ARE GETTING REALLY **BIG** IN YOUR FRONT GARDEN.

SCREECH!!

WOW. LOOK AT THAT LITTLE FELLOW SCOOT AROUND THE LOUNGE!

SLAM

NATURE AND WILDLIFE. YOU'RE EITHER A FAN OR YOU'RE NOT.

...AND WE'RE INTO THE **FINAL MINUTE** OF THE REFEREE'S OPTIONAL TIME! THE GAME'S ON A **KNIFE EDGE!**
--HE GETS THE BALL ON THE EDGE OF THE AREA--

HE BEATS ONE -- HE BEATS ANOTHER -- HE **SHOOTS!!** HE **SCORES!!** WHAT A GREAT **GOAL!!** IT'S THE **WINNER!!**
YES!!
LADUUMA!!
WHEEE!!
CLAP! CLAP! CLAP!!

NOW **THAT'S** WHAT I CALL A WORLD CUP SOCCER MATCH.

YOU KNOW MADAM, MAYBE IF YOU UNDERSTOOD HOW WORLD CUP SOCCER **WORKS**, YOU'D APPRECIATE IT MORE.
GO ON.

OKAY. FOR EXAMPLE, NEXT UP, THE USA <u>MEETS</u> GHANA.

HI. HOW YOU DOIN'?   HOWDY.   PLEASED TO MEET YOU.

YOU THINK SHE'S GETTING THIS?
I DON'T LIKE THE LOOK ON HER FACE.

THERE'S THE WHISTLE! ...AND THE REFEREE SHOWS A YELLOW CARD!!

YOU THINK I'M STUPID, EVE? YOU'VE BEEN DUSTING IN THE LOUNGE FOR THREE HOURS--JUST SO YOU CAN STAY HERE AND WATCH THE <u>WORLD CUP SOCCER</u>!

OKAY, FINE. I'LL GO DO THE **IRONING.**

AND HERE COMES THE FREE KICK...

MADAM &

BY STEPHEN FRANCIS & RICO

DEPARTURES: GATE 32

YOUR CALL.

WELCOME ABOARD FLIGHT 136 TO CAPE TOWN. PLEASE PAY ATTENTION TO THE FOLLOWING ANNOUNCEMENTS.

SINCE OUR FLIGHT WILL BE PARTIALLY OVER WATER, LIFE JACKETS ARE UNDER YOUR SEATS... THE EMERGENCY EXITS ARE CLEARLY MARKED.

IN THE UNLIKELY EVENT A **HIJACKER** DEMANDS WE FLY THE PLANE TO CAPE TOWN... WE TELL HIM THE PLANE IS ALREADY **GOING** TO CAPE TOWN.

... IF THAT DOESN'T WORK, SEVERAL **WELL-BUILT MEN** IN ROWS A - F...

... WILL JUMP UP AND **TACKLE** THE HIJACKER WHEN HE'S NOT LOOKING...

IN THE UNLIKELY EVENT THAT THIS IS **ALSO** UNSUCCESSFUL, **OXYGEN MASKS** WILL DROP FROM THE CEILING!

©RAPID PHASE-2006

... EITHER **SMACK** THE HIJACKER ON THE HEAD IN A **DOWNWARD MOTION**... OR SNAP HIM IN THE FACE WITH THE ELASTIC RUBBER STRAP.

FWAP!

FWAP!

FWAP!

AND, IN THE UNLIKELY EVENT THE **POLICE** SPECIAL FORCES ARE **RUDE** UPON BOARDING...

AIRCRAFT SAFETY INSTRUCTIONS ARE GETTING REALLY COMPLICATED THESE DAYS.

RIGHT-- THAT DOES IT!!

HEY!!

EVE--YOU HAVEN'T DONE *ANY* WORK FOR TWO WEEKS! I'M SORRY IT'S COME TO THIS--YOU HAVE A CHOICE: EITHER KEEPING YOUR JOB OR WATCHING TELEVISION!!

YOU CAN WORK FOR *ME*.

COOL. WHO'S PLAYING NEXT?

I HATE THE WORLD CUP!

THIS IS RIDICULOUS--AM I THE *ONLY* ONE IN SOUTH AFRICA *NOT* WATCHING THE WORLD CUP?!

MIELLLIES!

GO PORTUGAL! BEAT ENGLAND!

LET IT GO. PORTUGAL'S BEST PLAYERS ARE ALL SUSPENDED AND GERARD'S LOOKING REALLY GOOD.

...WHAT A PASS! --HE SHOOTS!! HE MISSES!!

AAARRGH!!

IS ENGLAND GOING TO BE OUT SOON?! HOW MUCH *MORE* OF THIS STUPID *WORLD CUP* THING DO I HAVE TO *PUT UP WITH*?!

SLAM!

TOUCHY, ISN'T SHE?

157

IT'S FUNNY HOW AN ISOLATED WORLD CUP INCIDENT OFTEN IMPACTS ON OUR DAILY LIVES.

©RAPID PHASE - 2006

EVE! WHERE'S MY GIN & TONIC?!

WHAT'S THE MATTER, MOM?

I TRIED TO **HEAD-BUTT** THE MIELIE-LADY... AND THREW MY **BACK** OUT.

©RAPID PHASE - 2006

AND HAVE YOU LEARNED YOUR **LESSON**?

NEVER HEAD-BUTT A MIELIE LADY UNLESS YOU DO A FEW **WARM-UP EXERCISES** FIRST.

THERE'S YOUR GIN & TONIC.

I'LL GET HER FOR THIS.

: SIGH :

CLICK. CLICK. CLICK. CLICK.

www.madamandeve.co.za

MAYBE WE SHOULD TURN THE TV ON.

...WHAT FOR? THERE'S **NOTHING** TO WATCH.

©RAPID PHASE - 2006

POST-WORLD CUP DEPRESSION SYNDROME.

: SIGH :

MADAM & EVE

BY STEPHEN FRANCIS & RICO

IF YOU'VE JUST JOINED US, YOU'RE WATCHING THE **SABC**... A FAIR AND INDEPENDENT PUBLIC BROADCASTER WITH <u>NO</u> POLITICAL AGENDA WHATSOEVER...

...BUT HEY, LET'S FACE IT. WHO **WOULDN'T** SUPPORT THE **ANC**?

TODAY'S TOP STORY: A COMMISSION HAS BEEN SET UP TO INVESTIGATE WHETHER THE SABC SOUGHT TO **GAG** COMMENTATORS ON A DOCUMENTARY **CRITICAL** OF **PRESIDENT MBEKI.**

...OH, SURE. LIKE WE'D REALLY <u>DO</u> THAT.

ANYWAY, THE SABC HAS, OF COURSE, **DENIED** ALL CHARGES, ISSUING THIS STATEMENT: "AT NO STAGE WAS <u>ANY</u> PRESSURE, POLITICAL OR OTHERWISE..."

"... EXERTED ON OUR EDITORIAL STAFF TO **CENSURE** CRITICAL REMARKS ABOUT **PRESIDENT MBEKI.** "

"...ESPECIALLY SINCE EVERYBODY KNOWS HE'S DOING SUCH A <u>GREAT</u> JOB!"

© RAPID PHASE 2006

...HOWEVER, IN THE INTEREST OF **FAIRNESS**... HERE ARE SEVERAL MEMBERS OF THE FREEDOM OF EXPRESSION INSTITUTE TO PRESENT AN **OPPOSING VIEWPOINT...**

THANK YOU. WE --

WHOAH!! SORRY, GUYS! OUT OF TIME! LET'S GO TO THE <u>WEATHER</u>!

TODAY'S OUTLOOK WILL BE **SUNNY**... THANKS TO THE SUBSIDISED HOUSING THE **ANC** PROVIDES FOR...

GWEN!

AND, IN OTHER NEWS... **JACOB ZUMA** IS SUING THE INDEPENDENT NEWSPAPER GROUP,...

...FOR PUBLISHING A SERIES OF **ZAPIRO CARTOONS** THAT ZUMA CLAIMS INJURED HIS DIGNITY AND REPUTATION.

©RAPID PHASE - 2006

...WHAT **MORON** TAKES **CARTOONS** SERIOUSLY?

www.madamandeve.co.za

HOW MANY JACOB ZUMAS DOES IT TAKE TO CHANGE A LIGHTBULB?

TWO. -- ONE TO CHANGE THE BULB... AND THE OTHER TO STRIP NAKED AND...**MMMPH!!**

©RAPID PHASE - 2006

SHE DIDN'T MEAN IT. SHE'S OVER EIGHTY! ...AND SHE DRINKS A **LOT** OF GIN & TONIC !!

WHAT'S THE MATTER?! AFRAID OF A LITTLE **LAWSUIT**?! *I WANT MY FREEDOM OF SPEECH DAMMIT!!*

HELLO! ROSES ARE RED VIOLETS ARE <u>BLUE</u> JACOB ZUMA IS SUING <u>YOU</u>!

YOU DAMAGED HIS REP YOU INJURED HIS <u>PRIDE</u> THERE'S NOWHERE TO RUN NOWHERE TO <u>HIDE</u>.

YOU'LL BE CHARGED WITH SLANDER (I'M PROUD TO <u>REPORT</u>) BETTER GET A LAWYER -- WE'LL SEE YOU IN <u>COURT</u>.

www.madamandeve.co.za ©RAPID PHASE 2006

WHO WAS AT THE DOOR?

WE GOT A ZUMA-GRAM.

AND IN OTHER NEWS, JACOB ZUMA SAYS HE WILL BE GOING AHEAD WITH HIS LAWSUIT... AGAINST CARTOONS, NEWSPAPERS AND RADIO STATIONS...

CAN YOU **BELIEVE** THIS? WHAT A ▬▬ ▬▬

OBVIOUSLY, HE ▬▬ ▬▬ ▬▬   YOU CAN SAY **THAT** AGAIN.

www.madamandeve.co.za

IT'S A SAD DAY WHEN ▬▬ ▬   HE PROBABLY ▬▬ ▬▬ ▬▬

APPROVED By LEGAL DEPARTMENT

AND IN TONIGHT'S TOP STORY, GAUTENG MEC FOR SAFETY AND SECURITY HAS PRESENTED A BOLD NEW 6 MONTH PLAN TO DRASTICALLY REDUCE CRIME...

NEWS

THIS WILL INCLUDE:
1) THE INCREASE OF POLICE VISIBILITY
2) MORE ROADBLOCKS...

NEWS

© RICO - 2006

3) THE STRATEGIC DEPLOYMENT OF OFFICERS IN PROBLEM AREAS... AND 4)...

NEWS

COULD YOU **STAND STILL** FOR ONE MINUTE?! I'M TRYING TO WATCH THIS!

NEWS

MADAM & EVE

BY STEPHEN FRANCIS & RICO

Panel 1: WHAT'S GOING ON? / I'VE... ASKED OUR **LAWYER** TO JOIN US THIS WEEK. YOU KNOW, JUST UNTIL THIS WHOLE CARTOON **LAWSUIT** THING BLOWS OVER.

Panel 2: OH, COME ON! WHO'D BE **STUPID** TO TRY AND CHALLENGE "FREEDOM OF SPEECH?" / AHEM!! COUGH! COUGH! COUGH!

Panel 3: FIRST OF ALL, I'D REFRAIN FROM USING "JACOB ZUMA"... OR THE NAMES "JACOB" OR "ZUMA" IN THE **SAME SENTENCE**.

Panel 4: WE CAN'T SAY **ZUMA**?! WHAT ARE WE SUPPOSED TO DO? / REPLACE IT WITH SOMETHING LESS ACTIONABLE, LIKE... "ZOOKEEPER"?

Panel 5: THE UPCOMING "ZOOKEEPER CORRUPTION TRIAL"... / COULD WORK... / I HATE IT!

Panel 6: I'D ALSO STAY AWAY FROM ANY REFERENCES TO "HIV" AND "TAKING A SHOWER"... "CONDOMS"... AND "CONSENTUAL SEX."

Panel 7: ...ALSO "WITNESS RELOCATION"... "LYING UNDER OATH"... "SCORPIONS"... "SEARCH AND SEIZURE"..."ARMS CONTRACTS"... AND "CORRUPTION."

Panel 8: ..."MASSAGES"... "MASSAGE OIL"... "ANYTHING TO **DO** WITH MASSAGES"..."KRUGERANDS IN BUCKETS"... AND "ILLEGITIMATE LOVE-CHILDREN".

Panel 9: HOW MANY "ZOOKEEPERS" DOES IT TAKE TO CHANGE A LIGHTBULB? / --AND NO LIGHTBULB JOKES EITHER.

Panel 10: THAT'S IT! I CAN'T **WORK** LIKE THIS! IT'S **MORONIC**! / I'D STAY AWAY FROM "MORONIC" TOO -- ALSO "STUPIDITY"... "INANE"... / I HAVE IRONING TO DO...

MADAM & EVE

BY STEPHEN FRANCIS & RICO

IN TONIGHT'S TOP STORY... GAUTENG'S **MEC FOR SAFETY AND SECURITY** PRESENTED A NEW SIX MONTH PLAN, PROMISING TO DRASTICALLY **REDUCE** CRIMINAL ACTIVITY.

1. INCREASE POLICE VISIBILITY

2. IMPROVE BASIC POLICE SKILLS

FREEZE!

INSTRUCTOR

3. MORE ROADBLOCKS

STOP

POLICE

4. IMPROVE CRIME INTELLIGENCE GATHERING

5. MORE ROADBLOCKS

6. STRATEGIC DEPLOYMENT OF OFFICERS IN PROBLEM AREAS

7. MORE ROADBLOCKS

8. IMPROVE FUNCTIONING OF 10111 CALL CENTRES

WELCOME TO THE SA POLICE SERVICE: FOR ARMED ROBBERIES, PRESS # 1. FOR HIJACKING, PRESS # 2. FOR BURGLARIES, PRESS # 3...

9. IMPROVE POLICE/COMMUNITY RELATIONS

YOU WANT ANOTHER?   NO THANKS, I'M ON DUTY.

MADAM & Eve

BY STEPHEN FRANCIS & RICO

AND IN OTHER NEWS -- "THE FRIENDS OF JACOB ZUMA" HAVE PROMISED TO **DOUBLE** THEIR **FUND-RAISING** EFFORTS TO PAY ALL LEGAL FEES FOR HIS UPCOMING CORRUPTION TRIAL.

JOIN THE FRIENDS OF EVE SISULU
Only 10 Rand

HOW MANY HAVE JOINED SO FAR?

THREE. BUT I'M FEELING REALLY **GOOD** ABOUT TODAY.

JOIN THE FRIENDS OF

IF I DECIDE TO JOIN, WHAT'S IN IT FOR ME?

BESIDES BEING MY FRIEND? YOU GET THIS "FRIENDS OF EVE SISULU" BUTTON TO WEAR EVERY DAY.

I THINK I'LL PASS.

SUIT YOURSELF. **NEXT!!**

"NEXT?"

HI. PERMIT US TO INTRODUCE OURSELVES. WE'RE THE "FRIENDS OF JACOB ZUMA."

GREAT. WE'VE BEEN EXPECTING YOU. FOLLOW ME.

HOLD THUMBS -- WE'RE THINKING OF COMBINING FORCES.

WHAT'S GOING ON? WHO ARE ALL THESE PEOPLE IN OUR BACK YARD?

"THE FRIENDS OF JACOB ZUMA" **MEET** "THE FRIENDS OF EVE SISULU."

IT SOUNDS LIKE A WRESTLING MATCH.

© RICO RAUSE - 2006

I AGREE THAT THE **POSTPONE-MENT** IS HURTING JACOB.

YES, HE'S SUFFERING PERSONAL AND ECONOMIC TRIAL PREJUDICE!

AS THE **FRIENDS OF JACOB ZUMA**... IT IS OUR DUTY TO ENSURE THAT ALL LEGAL FEES BE PAID.

ESPECIALLY IF THE **JUDGE** RULES AGAINST US.

SO WE'RE ALL AGREED. WE'LL **DOUBLE** OUR FUND-RAISING EFFORTS.

ABSOLUTELY.

THAT OKAY WITH YOU, JACOB?

HUH? SORRY-- SAY AGAIN? I GOT SOAP IN MY EAR!

© RAPID PHASE - 2006

AND IN OTHER NEWS, **THE FRIENDS OF JACOB ZUMA** SAID THEY NEED TO DOUBLE THEIR EFFORTS TO PAY LEGAL FEES FOR ZUMA'S UPCOMING CORRUPTION TRIAL... AND ARE LOOKING AT **EVERY POSSIBLE** WAY TO RAISE MONEY.

WHAT ARE WE GOING TO DO?

WHERE CAN WE GET **LOTS** OF **EASY MONEY** --FAST?

IT'S NOT FAIR.

www.madamandeve.co.za

YEAH... "GOVERNMENT ARMS DEALS..." THERE'S NEVER ONE AROUND WHEN YOU REALLY **NEED** ONE.

© RAPID PHASE - 2006

...WHAT?

MADAM & Eve

BY STEPHEN FRANCIS & RICO

...AND IF YOU ACT **NOW**, YOU'LL RECEIVE THIS **FREE** SET OF **STEAK KNIVES!** HURRY! OPERATORS ARE STANDING BY TO TAKE YOUR CALL! --<u>TERMS</u> AND <u>CONDITIONS</u> APPLY!

AND TODAY'S TOP STORY... **CYRIL RAMAPHOSA** HAS ANNOUNCED HE HAS ABSOLUTELY **NO INTEREST** IN RUNNING FOR ANC PRESIDENT. --<u>TERMS</u> AND <u>CONDITIONS</u> APPLY.

EVE! YOU FORGOT TO DO THE WASHING AND IRONING.

I'M HAPPY TO DO THE LAUNDRY RIGHT AWAY, MADAM...

...<u>TERMS</u> AND <u>CONDITIONS</u> APPLY.

AND WHAT'S **THAT** SUPPOSED TO MEAN?

IT MEANS THE TERM "HAPPY TO DO THE LAUNDRY,"...

...ONLY APPLIES UNTIL **AFTER** MY TEA BREAK.

FINE. THEN DO THE LAUNDRY **AFTER** YOUR TEA BREAK.

I WOULD. --IF IT WASN'T FOR THE OTHER **CONDITION.**

<u>WHAT</u> OTHER CONDITION?

MY OFFER TO "HAPPILY DO THE LAUNDRY" IS <u>ONLY</u> VALID TUESDAYS AFTER <u>TEN</u>...

...OR THURSDAYS <u>BEFORE</u> ELEVEN.

WELL, IT'S ALMOST THE **END** OF THE **MONTH.** I'LL GO AND GET YOUR **WAGES** READY.

...TERMS AND CONDITIONS APPLY.

I HAD A FEELING SHE WAS GOING TO SAY THAT.

MADAM & EVE

BY STEPHEN FRANCIS & RICO

A DEFENCE SPOKESMAN SAID THAT, ALTHOUGH THE VERTICALLY DEPLOYED ANTIPERSONNEL DEVICE EXPLODED... COLLATERAL DAMAGE WAS LIMITED WITH ONLY A FEW METABOLICALLY-CHALLENGED PEOPLE REPORTED.

HMPH. POLITICAL CORRECTNESS.

I KNOW WHAT YOU MEAN. IT MAKES ME WANT TO INVOLUNTARILY SPASM AND EJECT MY PRE-DIGESTED STOMACH CONTENTS.

EVE!! HAVE YOU DONE THE DISHES YET?

NOT YET...

...I'M STILL BUSY WITH THE HYGENIC GROUND DETRITUS REMOVAL SUCTION DEVICE!

THEN I THOUGHT I'D ATTEND TO THE WEEKLY FABRIC APPAREL CLEANSING AND RESTORATIVE RITUAL.

OF COURSE, I MIGHT WORK A LITTLE **HARDER**... IF YOU EVER GAVE ME AN INCRIMENTAL AGGREGATED RENUMERATION UPGRADE.

I WOULD... IF I WASN'T SO GENEROSITY-CHALLENGED AND FISCALLY RETENTIVE.

ANYWAY-- **IT'S AFTER FIVE!!**

I KNOW, I KNOW-- YOU WANT YOUR DAILY CHILLED MULTI-INGREDIENT INTOXICATING MOOD ENHANCER!

--AND MAKE IT A TWO HUNDRED PERCENT ALCOHOLICALLY BOOSTED LIBATION!!

COMING RIGHT UP...

...JUST AS SOON AS I'VE COMPLETED MY HEATED BEVERAGE-ENHANCED RECUPERATIVE TIME PERIOD.

© RAPID PHASE · 2006

THE HIGH SEAS...

A LONE **PIRATE**...SEEKING PILLAGE AND PLUNDER

BUT CLIMBING ABOARD **THIS** SHIP... MAY BE **HARDER** THAN IT LOOKS.

ZAP! CRACKLE! POP!

...GOOD THING WE INVESTED IN THAT **ELECTRIFIED FENCE.**

YES! IT'S THE RETURN OF THE DREADED
MADAMS OF THE CARIBBEAN!!

MADAMS OF THE CARIBBEAN

LOOK SHARP, ME HEARTIES! WE'RE ABOUT TO DOCK!

www.madamandeve.co.za

OKAY! GOOD. LEFT A BIT! KEEP GOING! STRAIGHT! STRAIGHT!

DAMN. A FLOATING **PARKING ATTENDANT.** ANYONE HAVE TWO RAND?

...LEFT MY PURSE AT HOME.

NO CHANGE.

I JUST GAVE TO THE LAST GUY.

MADAMS OF THE CARIBBEAN

SWAB THE DECKS AND LOAD THE WASHING!!

AYE, AYE, CAPTAIN!

www.madamandeve.co.za

MAN THE FEATHER DUSTERS!! LOWER THE VACUUM!!

AYE, AYE, CAPTAIN!

CASH THE PAYCHEQUE!!

...JUST JOKING. **HOIST THE IRONING BOARD!!**

ONE OF THESE DAYS... **MUTINY.**

MADAMS OF THE CARIBBEAN

POLLY WANT A CRACKER? ·SQUAWK·

·SQUAWK· MIELLLIES!!

© RAPID PHASE 2006

I TOLD HER NOT TO BUY A **USED** PARROT.

·SQUAWK·

www.madamandeve.co.za

MADAMS OF THE CARIBBEAN

WELL, WELL. LOOK WHO'S DECIDED TO COME TO WORK!

...AND YOU CALL YOURSELF A **DOMESTIC SAILOR**?!

www.madamandeve.co.za

THIS SHIP'S A **MESS!** THE DECKS HAVEN'T BEEN SWABBED FOR <u>DAYS</u>!

...NOT TO MENTION DUSTING THE <u>SAILS</u>!

© RAPID PHASE · 2006

AND ANOTHER THING--

NOW I KNOW WHY THEY CALL IT A **CROW'S NEST.**

BRIDGE

STERN

PORT

KEEL

DRAFT

SQUALL

ABOARD

OVERBOARD

WAKE

HOLD

GUNWALE

CAPSIZE

By Stephen Francis & Rico

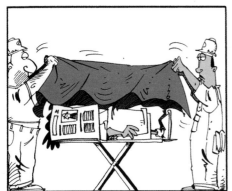

PLEASE BE PATIENT

The **Madam & Eve** Cartoon strip is under renovation and reconstruction. We apologise for any inconvenience.

Madam & Eve will be back next week.